21ST CENTURY I

CW00418477

EXCLUSIVE DISTRIBUTORS:
MUSIC SALES LIMITED
8/9 FRITH STREET, LONDON W1D 3JB,
ENGLAND.
MUSIC SALES PTY LIMITED
120 ROTHSCHILD AVENUE, ROSEBERY,
NSW 2018, AUSTRALIA.

ORDER NO. AM981409
ISBN 1-84449-818-2
THIS BOOK © COPYRIGHT 2004
BY WISE PUBLICATIONS.

COMPILED BY NICK CRISPIN.
MUSIC ARRANGED BY MATT COWE.
MUSIC PROCESSED BY PAUL EWERS MUSIC DESIGN.

COVER DESIGN BY FRESH LEMON.
PRINTED IN MALTA BY
INTERPRINT LIMITED.

YOUR GUARANTEE OF QUALITY:
AS PUBLISHERS, WE STRIVE TO PRODUCE EVERY
BOOK TO THE HIGHEST COMMERCIAL STANDARDS.
THE MUSIC HAS BEEN FRESHLY ENGRAVED AND
THE BOOK HAS BEEN CAREFULLY DESIGNED
TO MINIMISE AWKWARD PAGE TURNS AND TO
MAKE PLAYING FROM IT A REAL PLEASURE.
PARTICULAR CARE HAS BEEN GIVEN TO
SPECIFYING ACID-FREE, NEUTRAL-SIZED
PAPER MADE FROM PULPS WHICH HAVE
NOT BEEN ELEMENTAL CHLORINE BLEACHED.
THIS PULP IS FROM FARMED SUSTAINABLE
FORESTS AND WAS PRODUCED WITH
SPECIAL REGARD FOR THE ENVIRONMENT.
THROUGHOUT, THE PRINTING AND BINDING HAVE
BEEN PLANNED TO ENSURE A STURDY,
ATTRACTIVE PUBLICATION WHICH
SHOULD GIVE YEARS OF ENJOYMENT.
IF YOUR COPY FAILS TO MEET OUR HIGH STANDARDS,
PLEASE INFORM US AND WE WILL GLADLY REPLACE IT.

www.musicsales.com

WISE PUBLICATIONS
LONDON / NEW YORK / PARIS / SYDNEY / COPENHAGEN / BERLIN / MADRID / TOKYO

18.9V

GUITAR TABLATURE EXPLAINED

Guitar music can be notated three different ways: on a musical stave, in tablature, and in rhythm slashes

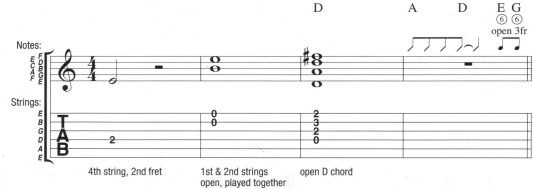

RHYTHM SLASHES are written above the stave. Strum chords in the rhythm indicated. Round noteheads indicate single notes.

THE MUSICAL STAVE shows pitches and rhythms and is divided by lines into bars. Pitches are named after the first seven letters of the alphabet.

TABLATURE graphically represents the guitar fingerboard. Each horizontal line represents a string, and each number represents a fret.

4th string, 2nd fret   1st & 2nd strings open, played together   open D chord

DEFINITIONS FOR SPECIAL GUITAR NOTATION

SEMI-TONE BEND: Strike the note and bend up a semi-tone (1/2 step).

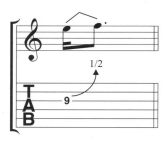

WHOLE-TONE BEND: Strike the note and bend up a whole-tone (whole step).

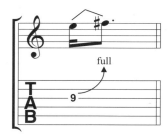

GRACE NOTE BEND: Strike the note and bend as indicated. Play the first note as quickly as possible.

QUARTER-TONE BEND: Strike the note and bend up a 1/4 step.

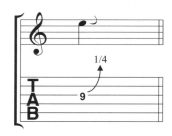

BEND & RELEASE: Strike the note and bend up as indicated, then release back to the original note.

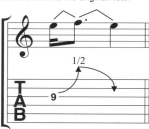

COMPOUND BEND & RELEASE: Strike the note and bend up and down in the rhythm indicated.

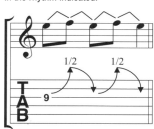

PRE-BEND: Bend the note as indicated, then strike it.

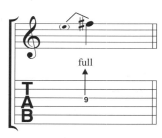

PRE-BEND & RELEASE: Bend the note as indicated. Strike it and release the note back to the original pitch.

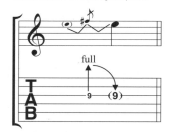

HAMMER-ON: Strike the first note with one finger, then sound the second note (on the same string) with another finger by fretting it without picking.

PULL-OFF: Place both fingers on the notes to be sounded, strike the first note and without picking, pull the finger off to sound the second note.

LEGATO SLIDE (GLISS): Strike the first note and then slide the same fret-hand finger up or down to the second note. The second note is not struck.

MUFFLED STRINGS: A percussive sound is produced by laying the fret hand across the string(s) without depressing, and striking them with the pick hand.

NATURAL HARMONIC: Strike the note while the fret-hand lightly touches the string directly over the fret indicated.

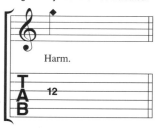

PICK SCRAPE: The edge of the pick is rubbed down (or up) the string, producing a scratchy sound.

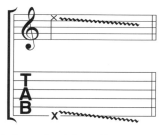

PALM MUTING: The note is partially muted by the pick hand lightly touching the string(s) just before the bridge.

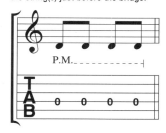

SHIFT SLIDE (GLISS & RESTRIKE): Same as legato slide, except the second note is struck.

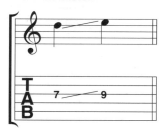

NOTE: The speed of any bend is indicated by the music notation and tempo.

ALL THESE THINGS THAT I'VE DONE

WORDS & MUSIC BY BRANDON FLOWERS, DAVE KEUNING, MARK STOERMER & RONNIE VANNUCCI

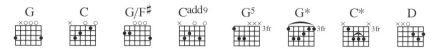

To match recording tune all strings down one semitone

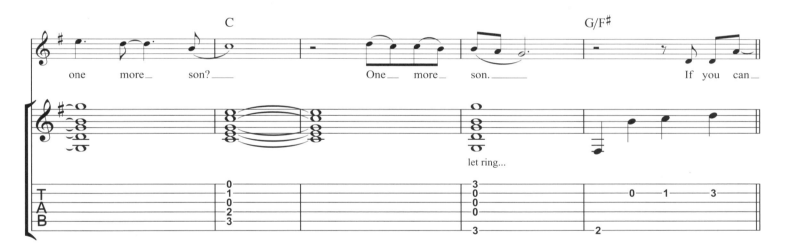

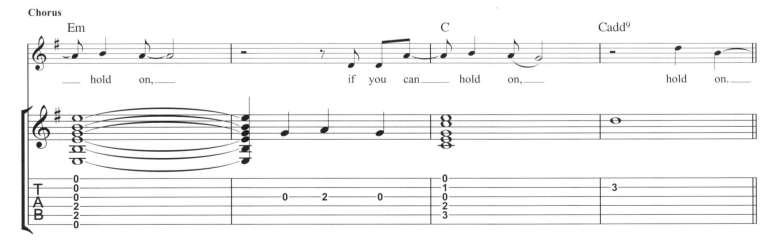

Interlude

*chords implied by harmony

Verse

2. I wan-na stand up,___ I wan-na let go.___ You know, you know, no
3. An-oth-er head-ache,___ an-oth-er heart-break.___ I'm so much old-er

2° play Fig.1

tacet 1°

Gtr. 1 (elec.)

f w/fuzz
Fig. 1...

...Fig. 1 ends

4

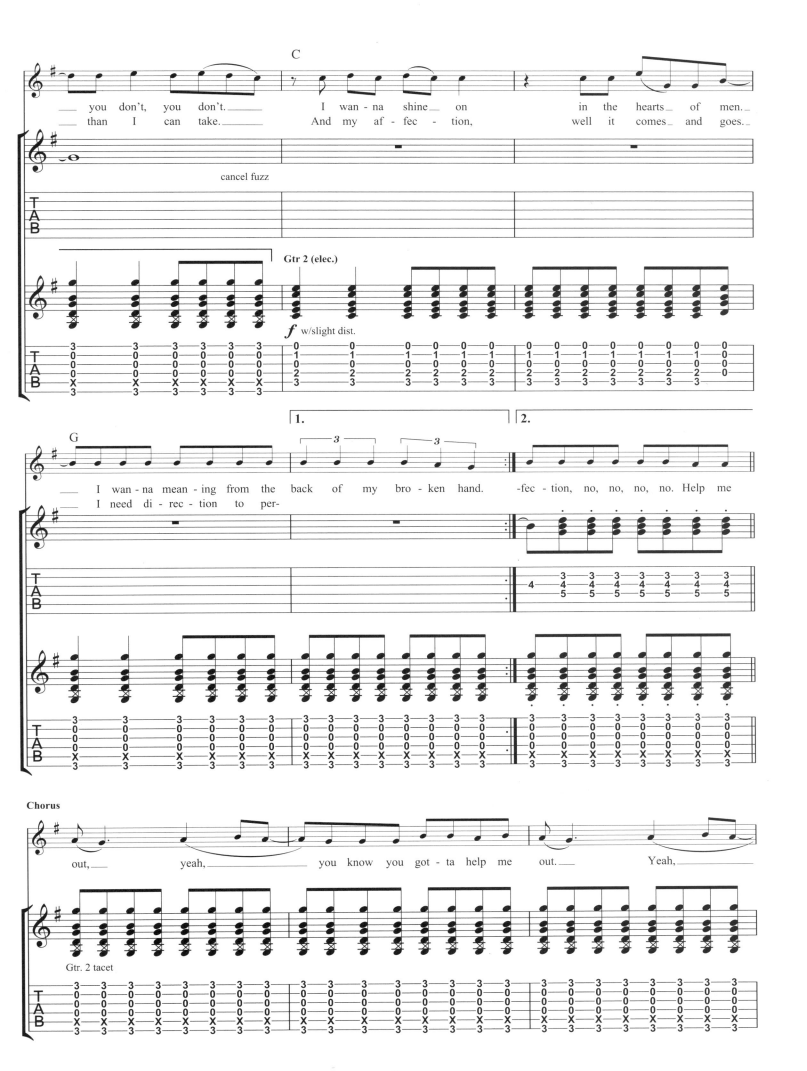

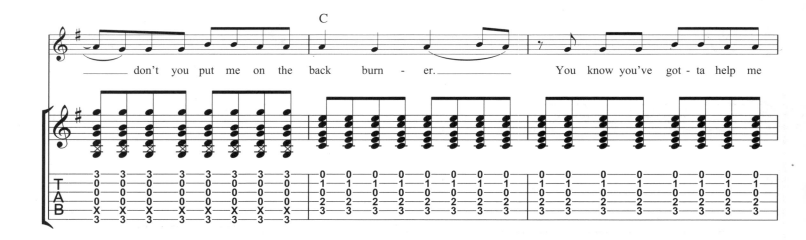

_____ don't you put me on the back burn - er. _____ You know you've got - ta help me

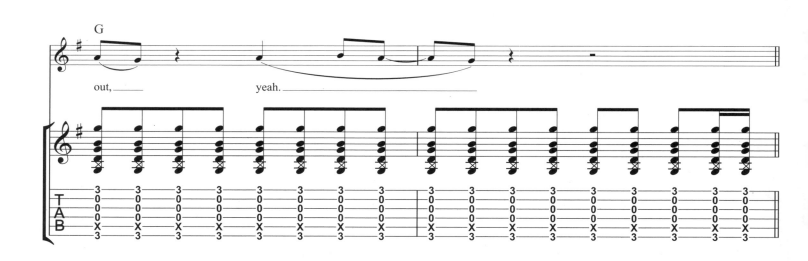

out, _____ yeah. _____

Verse

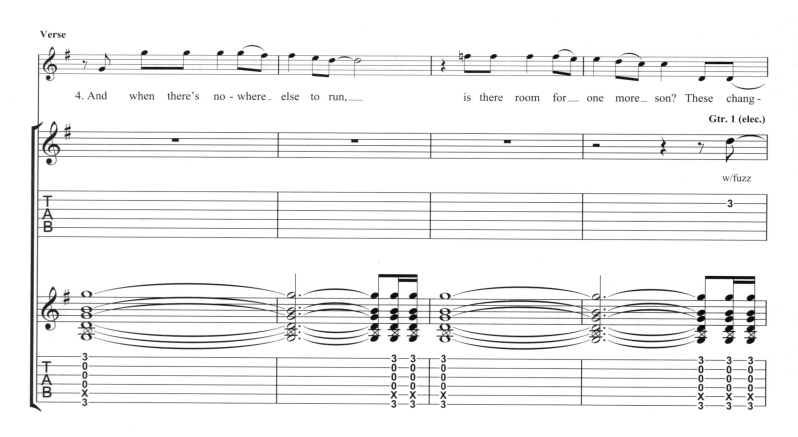

4. And when there's no - where_ else to run, _____ is there room for_ one more_ son? These chang -

Gtr. 1 (elec.)

w/fuzz

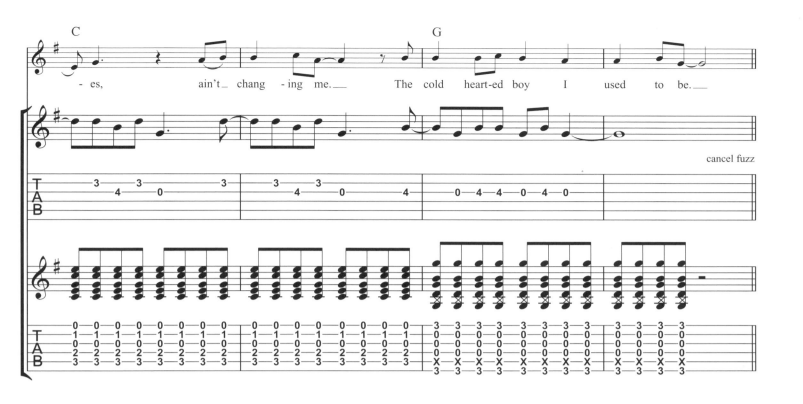

Chorus

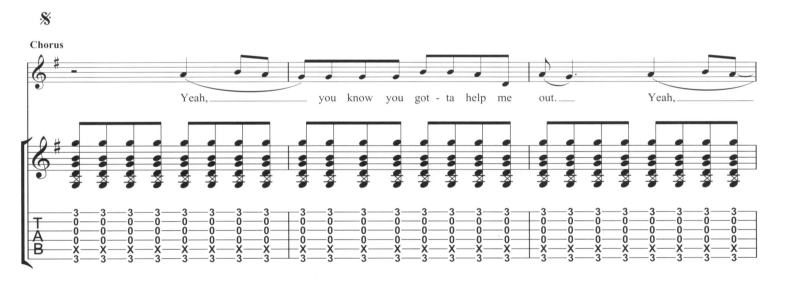

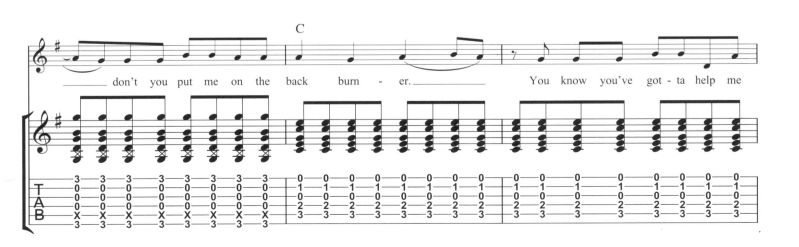

8

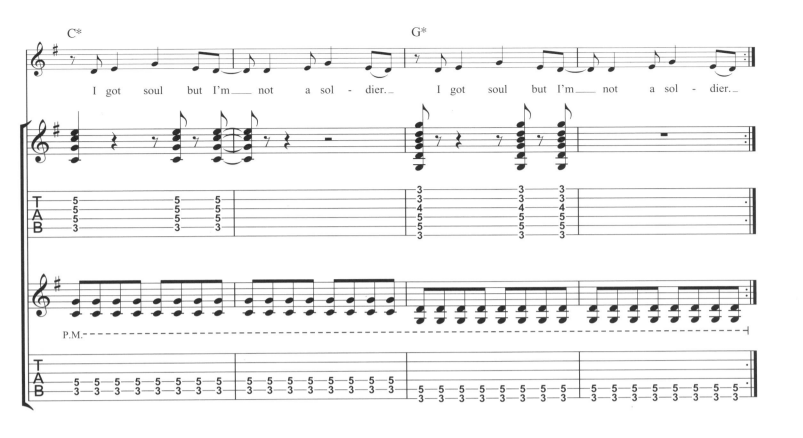

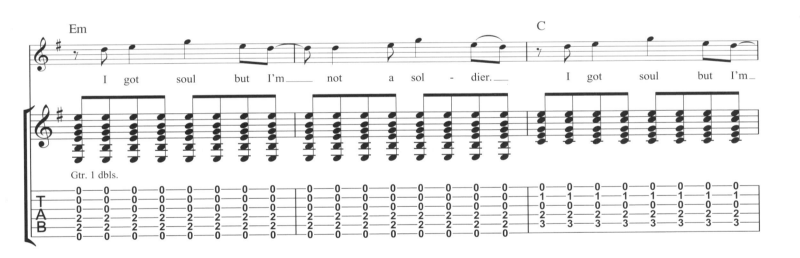

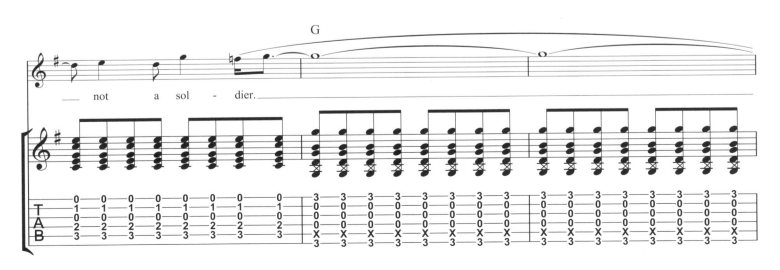

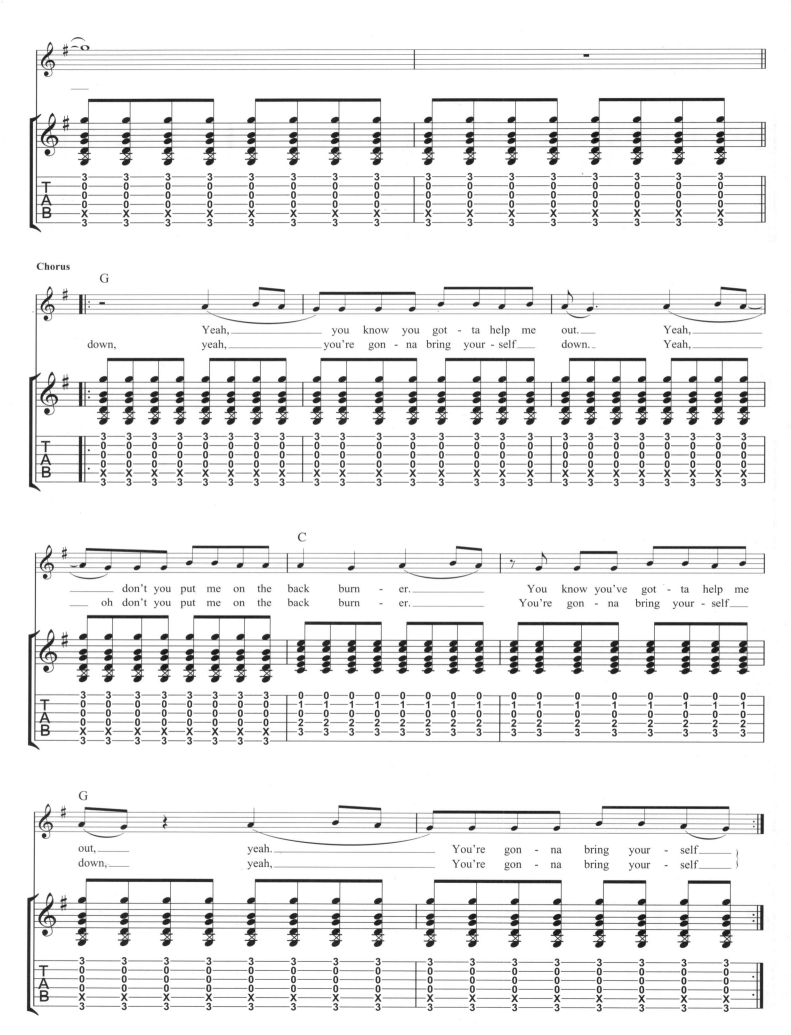

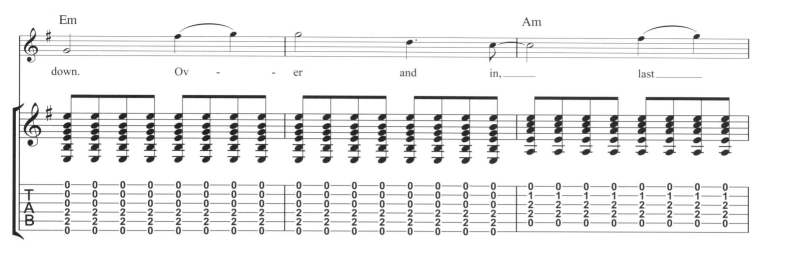

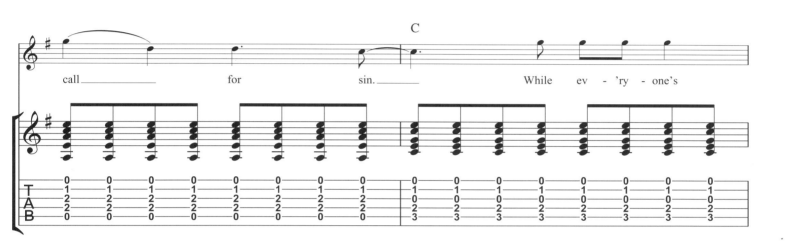

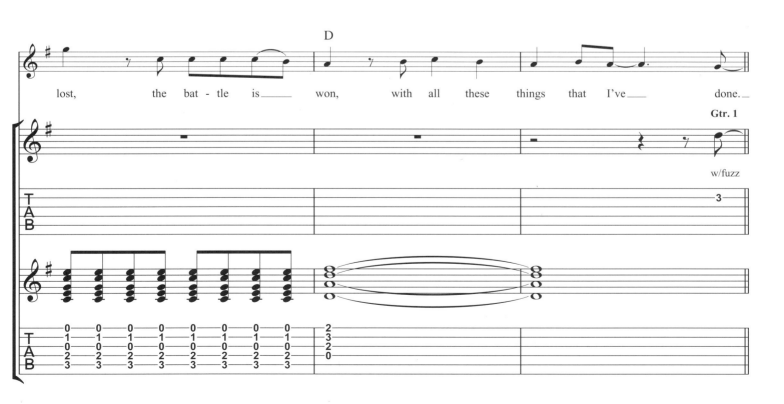

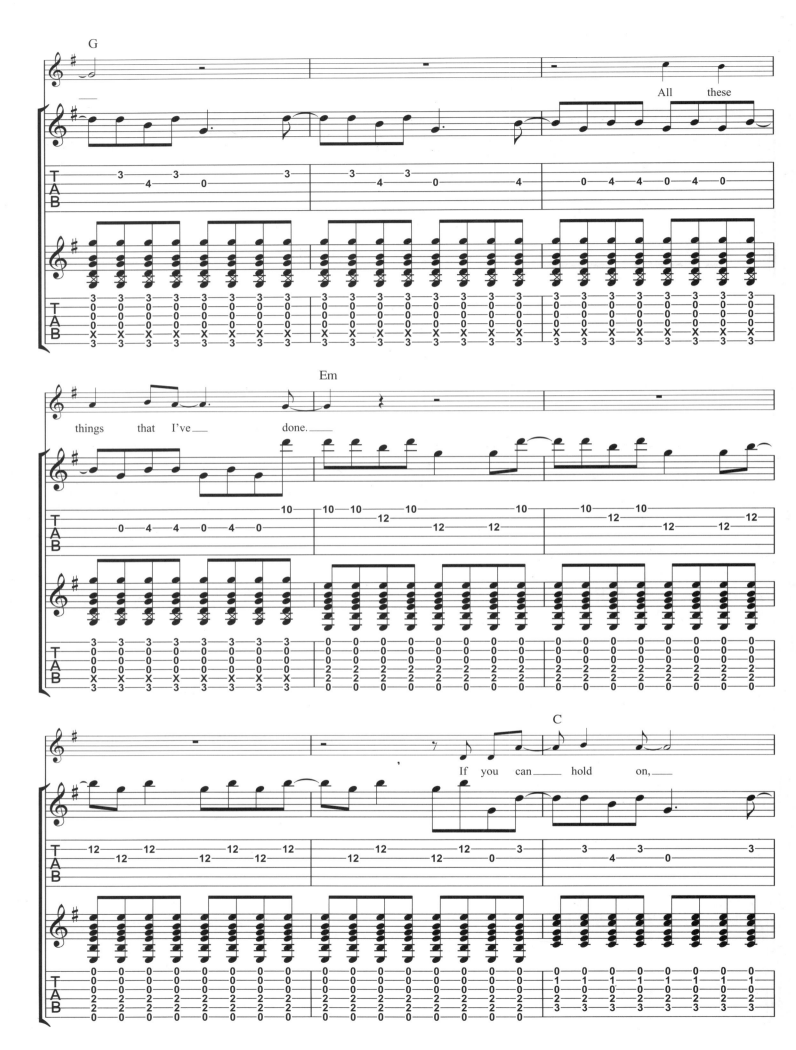

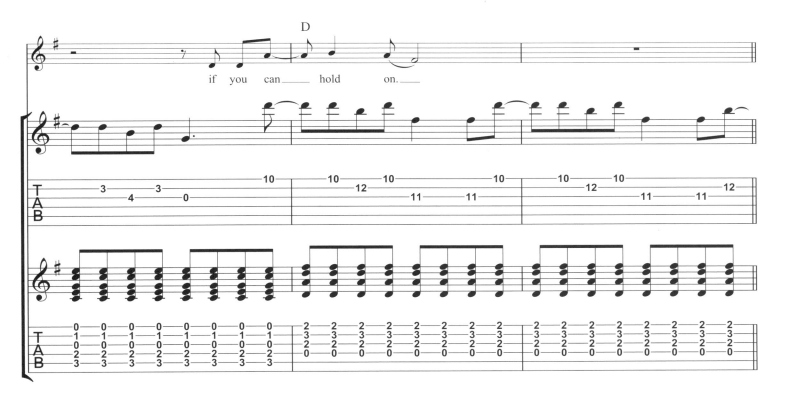

if you can   hold   on.

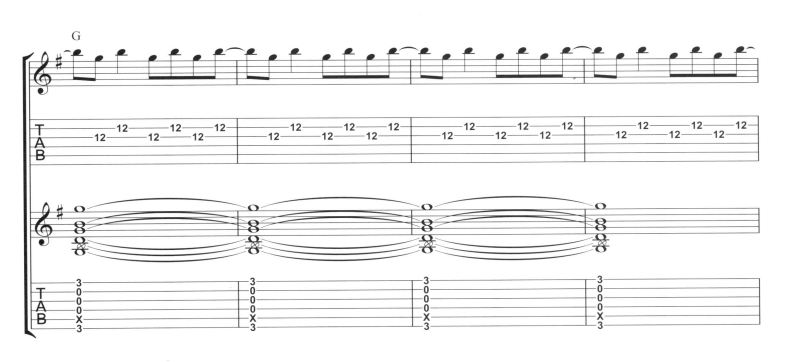

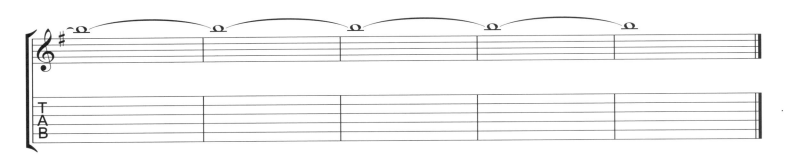

AMERICAN IDIOT
WORDS & MUSIC BY BILLIE JOE ARMSTRONG, FRANK WRIGHT & MICHAEL PRITCHARD

1. Don't wan-na be an A-me-ri-can i-di-ot,
2. Well may-be I'm_ the fag-got A-me-ri-ca,

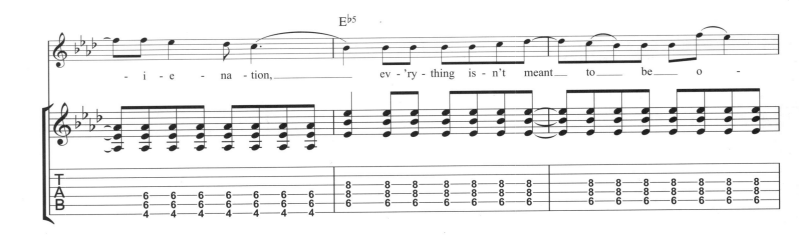

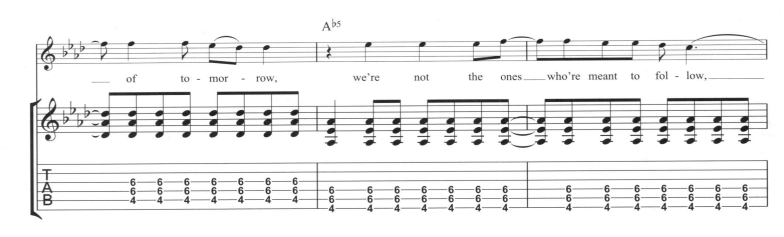

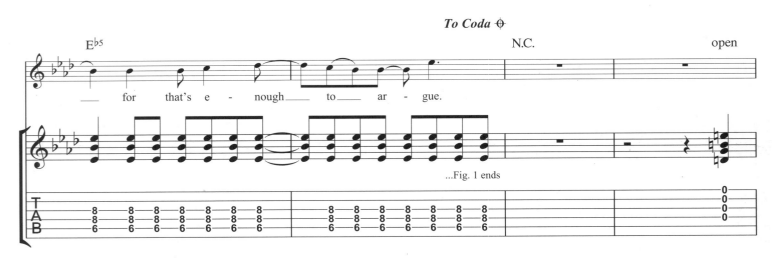

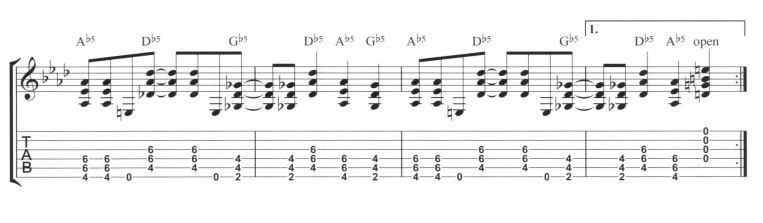

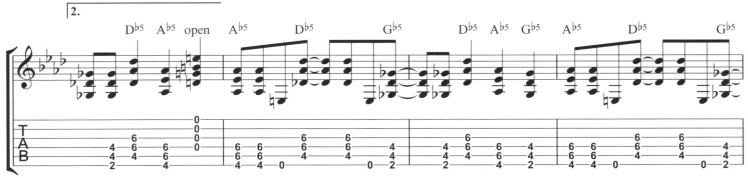

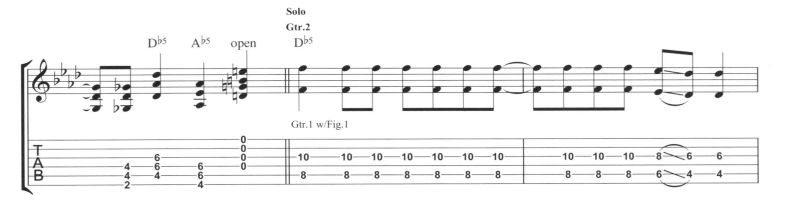

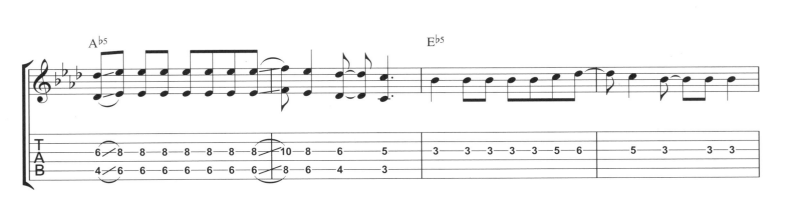

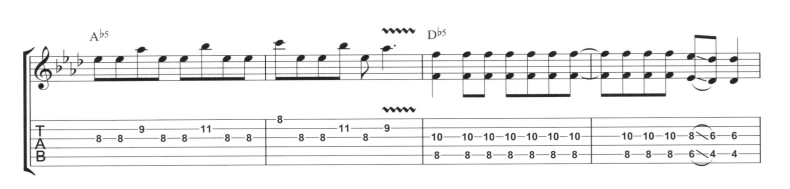

BUTTERFLIES & HURRICANES

WORDS & MUSIC BY MATTHEW BELLAMY, CHRIS WOLSTENHOLME & DOMINIC HOWARD

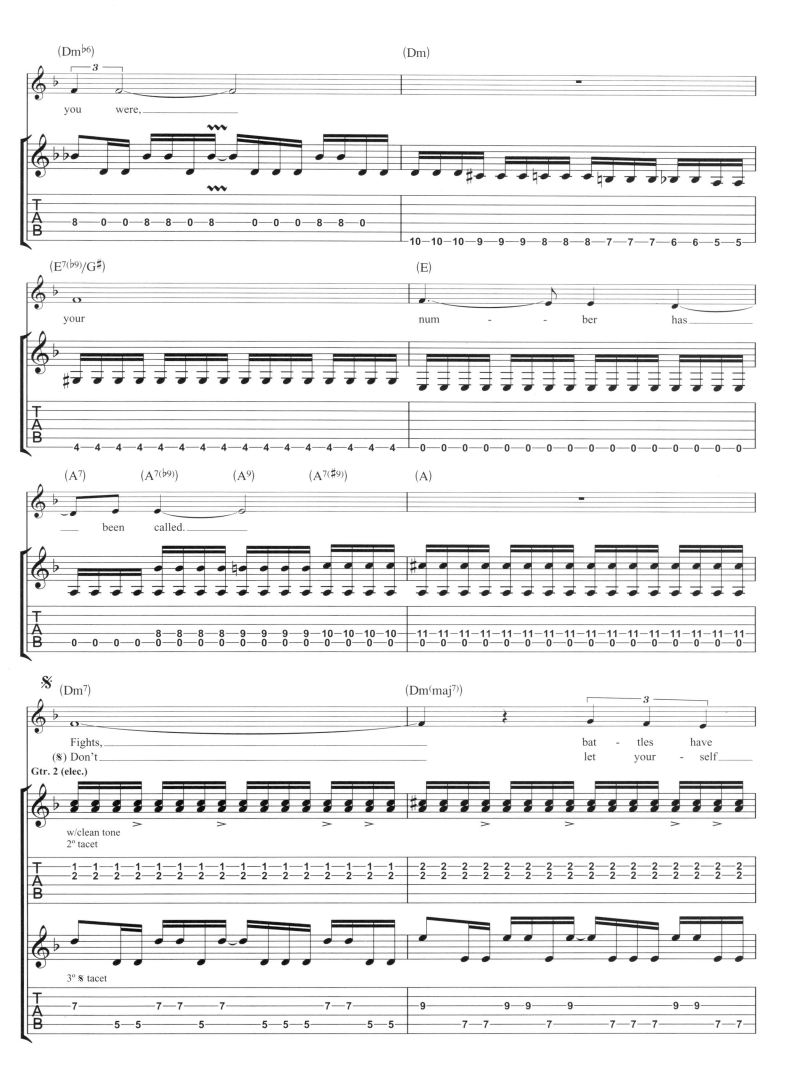

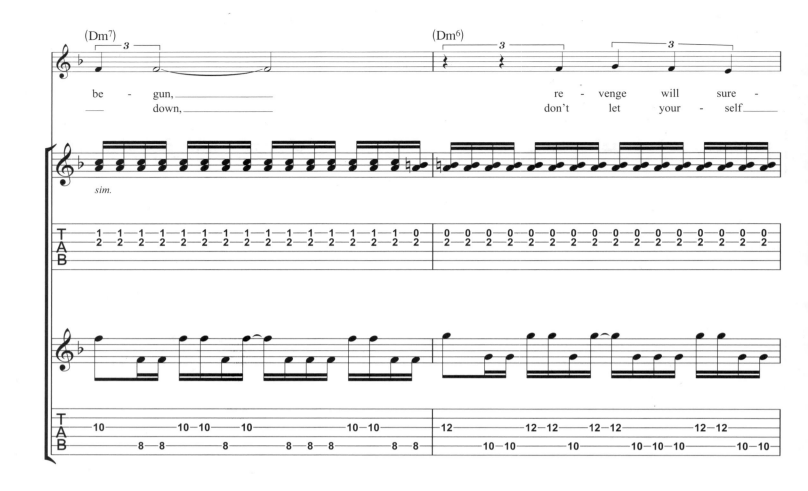

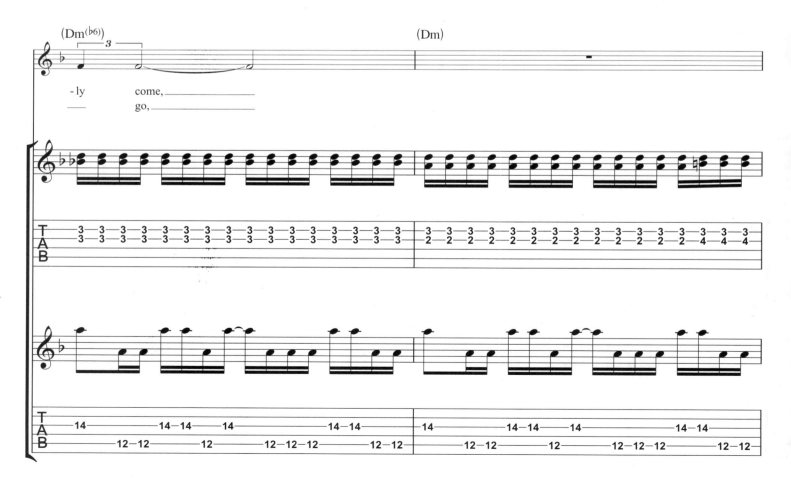

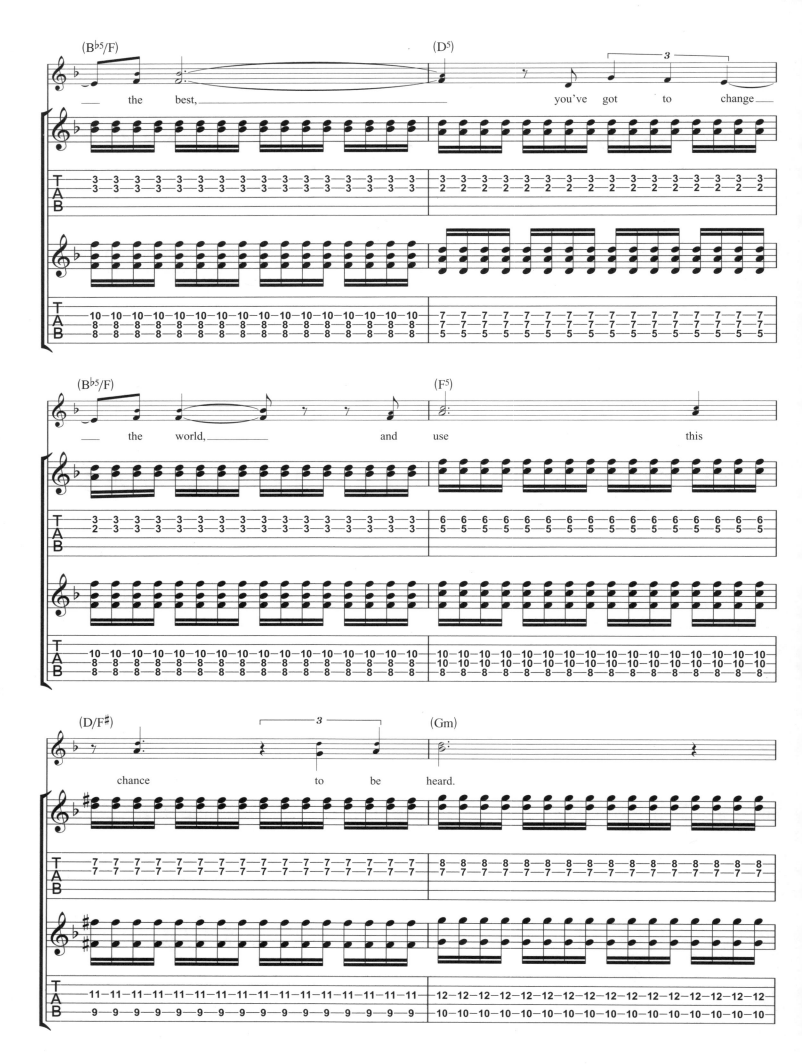

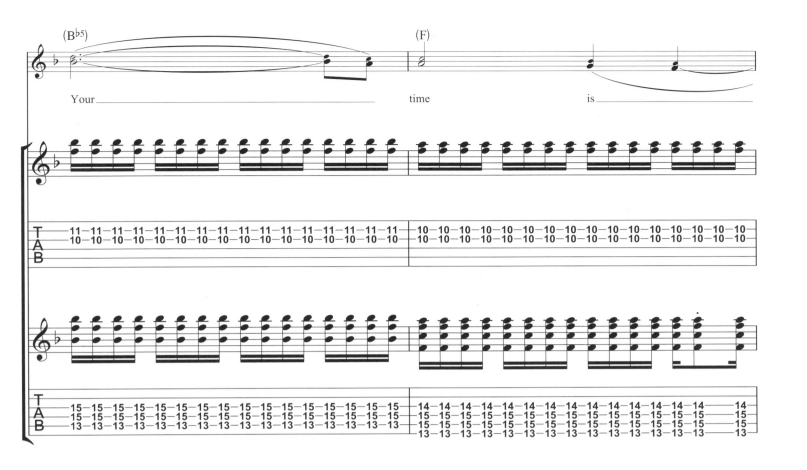

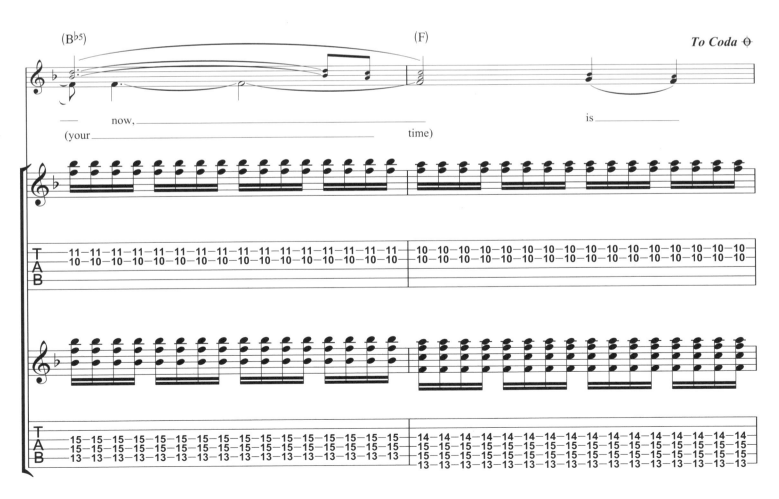

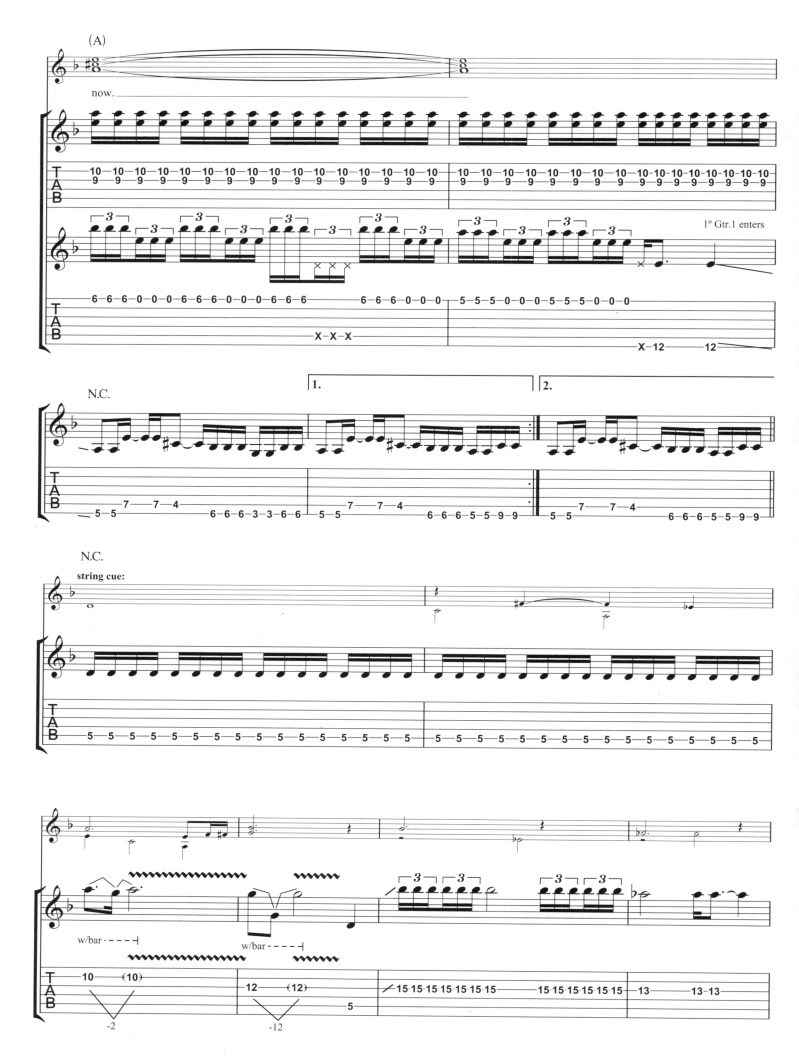

D.S. al Coda

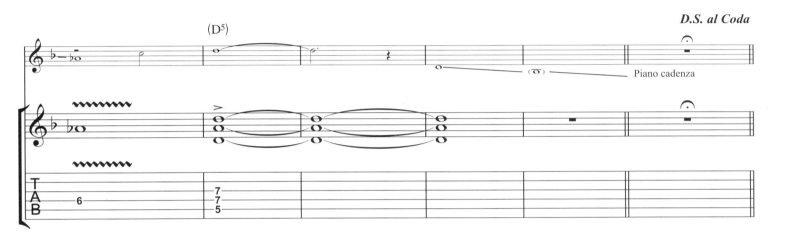

⊕ *Coda*

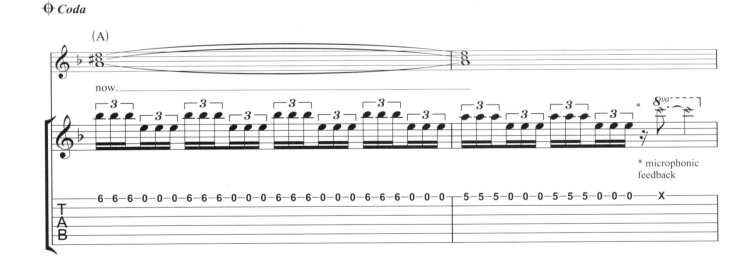

ARE YOU GONNA BE MY GIRL

WORDS & MUSIC BY NIC CESTER & CAMERON MUNCEY

28

1. Said one two three, take my hand and come with me be-cause you
one two three, take my hand and come with me be-cause you

look so fine that I real-ly wan-na make you mine._____ I say you

look so fine that I real-ly wan-na make you mine._____ I say you

look so fine that I real-ly wan-na make you mine._____ Well

look so fine that I real-ly wan-na make you mine._____ Well

four five six, come on___ and get your kicks, now you don't need a-mon-ey when you look like that, do you hon-ey?___

four five six, come on___ and get your kicks, now you don't need a-mon-ey with a face like that, do you?

cont. in stave

Gtr. 2

Big___ black boots,

Gtrs. 1+2

long___ brown___ hair, she's___ so sweet with___ her get___ back stare.

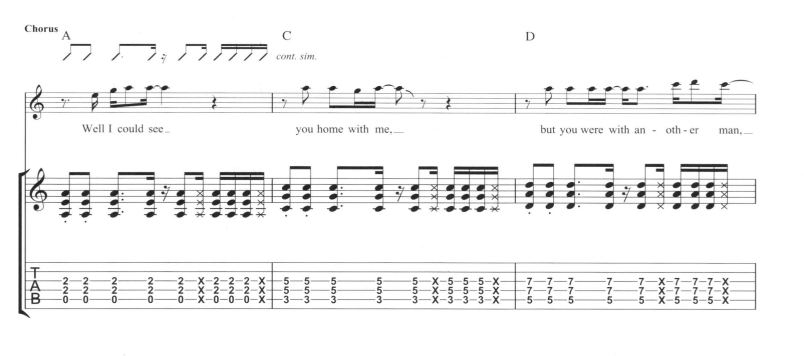

Well I could see__ you home with me,__ but you were with an-oth-er man,__

_____ yeah.__ I____know we ain't__got much to say,__

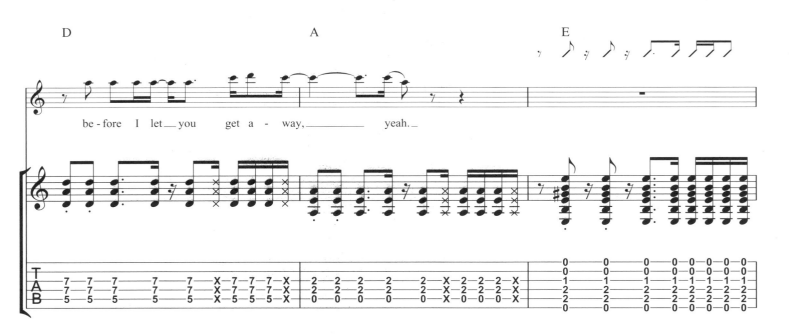

be-fore I let__you get a-way,_____ yeah.__

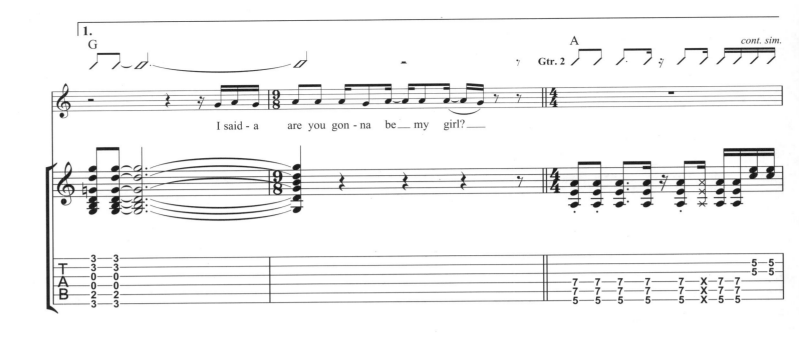

I said - a   are you gon - na   be ___ my   girl? ___

2. Well it's a

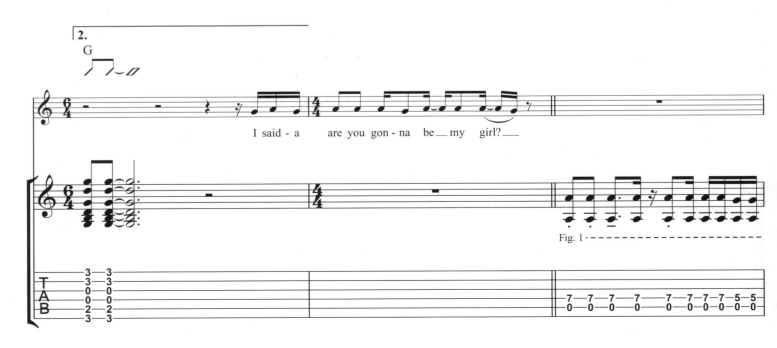

I said - a   are you gon - na   be ___ my   girl? ___

Fig. 1 -

I___know we ain't got much to say,___ be - fore I let___you get a - way,___

_____ yeah.___ a - be my girl,___ be___ my girl,

are you gon - na be___my girl?_____ Yeah.

CALIFORNIA

WORDS & MUSIC BY ALEX GREENWALD & JASON SCHWARTZMAN

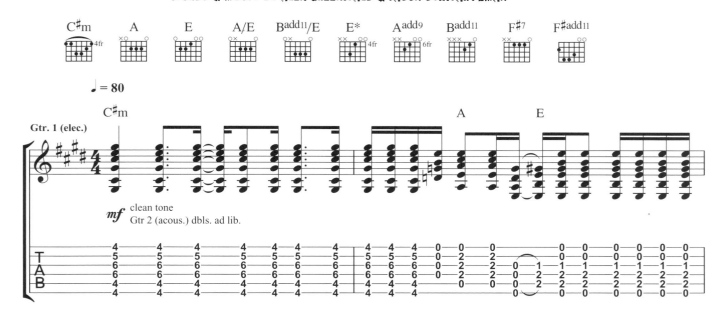

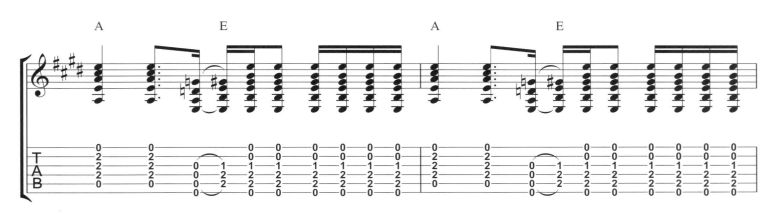

1. We've been on the run, driv-ing in the sun, Look-ing out for num-ber one.____
2. On the ste-re-o, lis-ten as we go. No-thing's gon-na stop me now.____ Ca - li - for-

-nia here___ we come,___ right back where we start-ed from._____ { Well,
{ The

Gtr. 3 *(2° only)*

let ring...

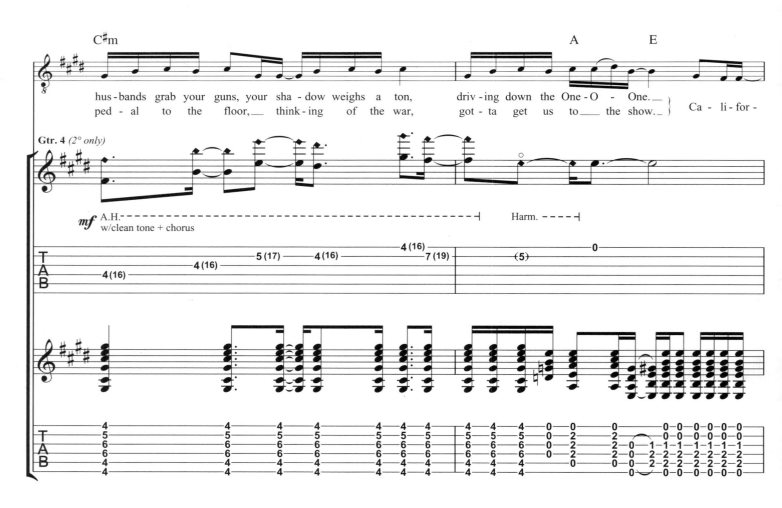

hus-bands grab your guns, your sha-dow weighs a ton, driv-ing down the One-O-One.___ } Ca-li-for-
ped-al to the floor,___ think-ing of the war, got-ta get us to___ the show.___ }

Gtr. 4 *(2° only)*

mf A.H.--- Harm. ------

w/clean tone + chorus

Ca - li - for - ia, Ca - li - for - nia, here we come.

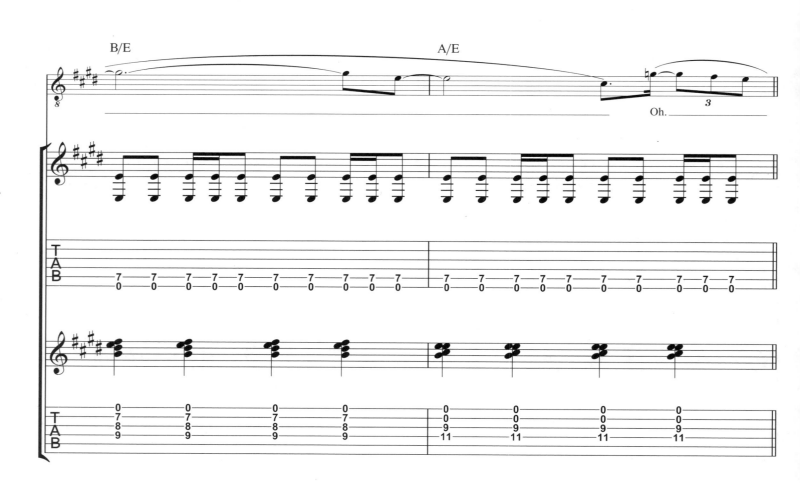

Oh.

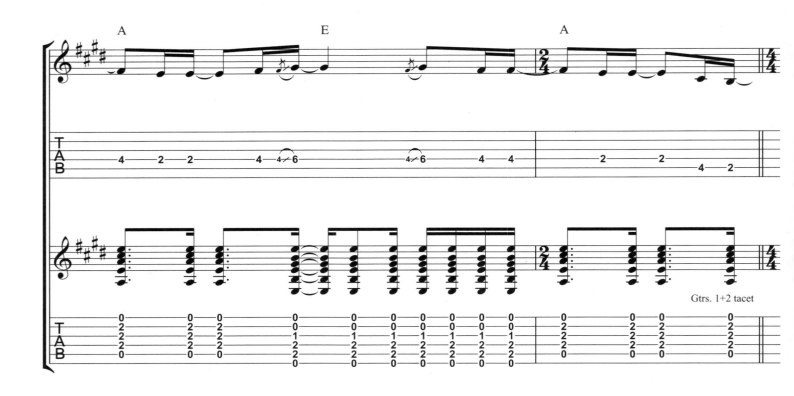

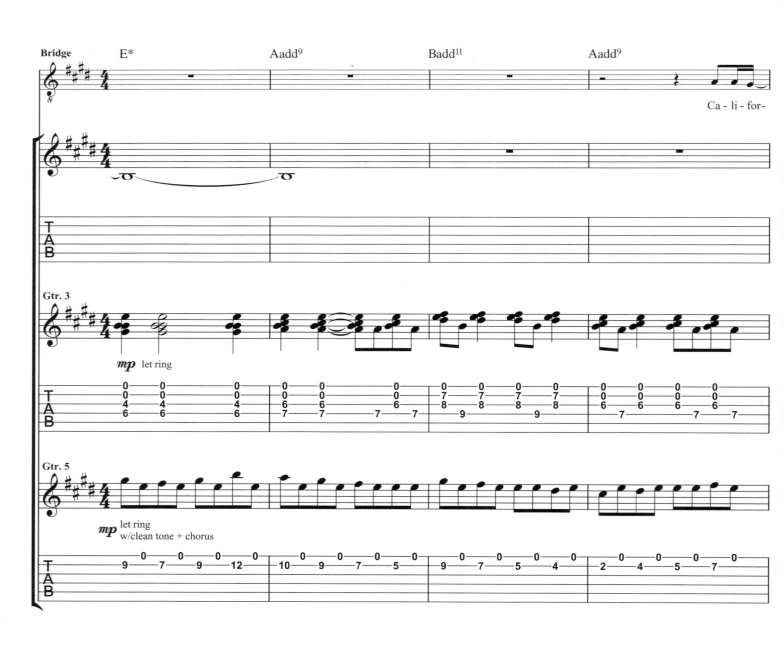

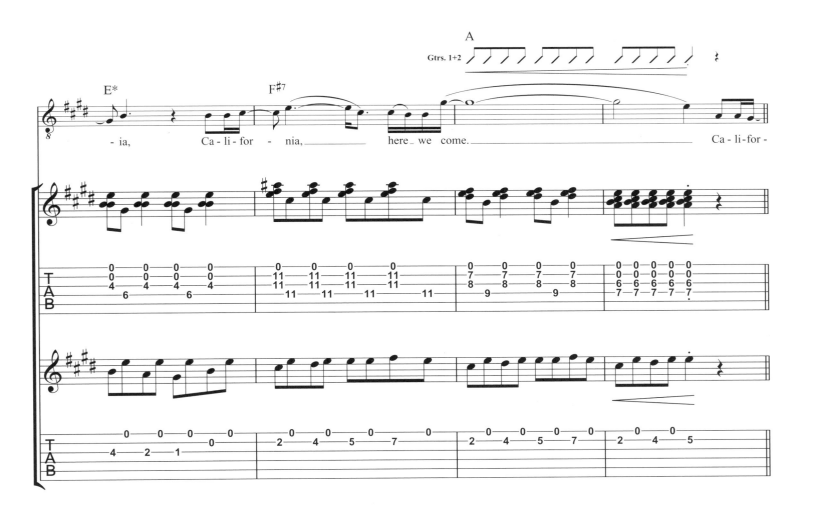

41

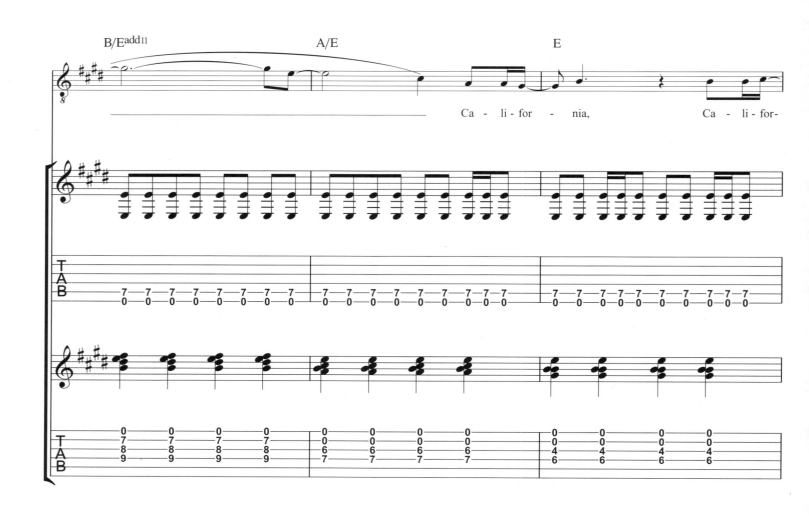

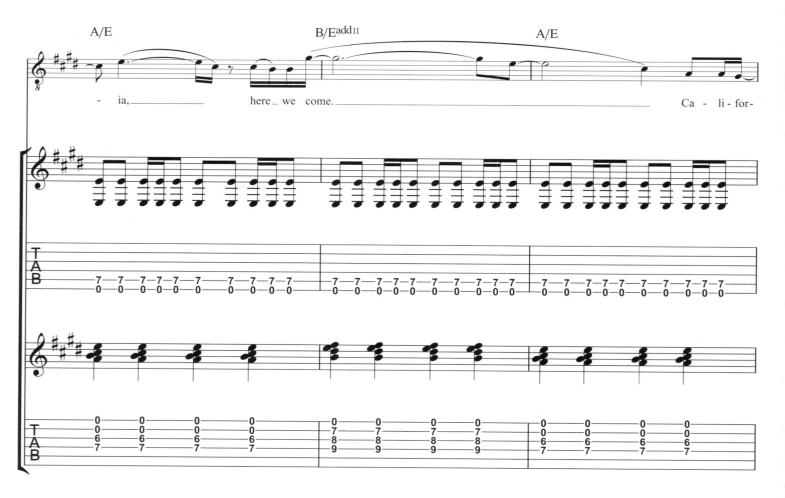

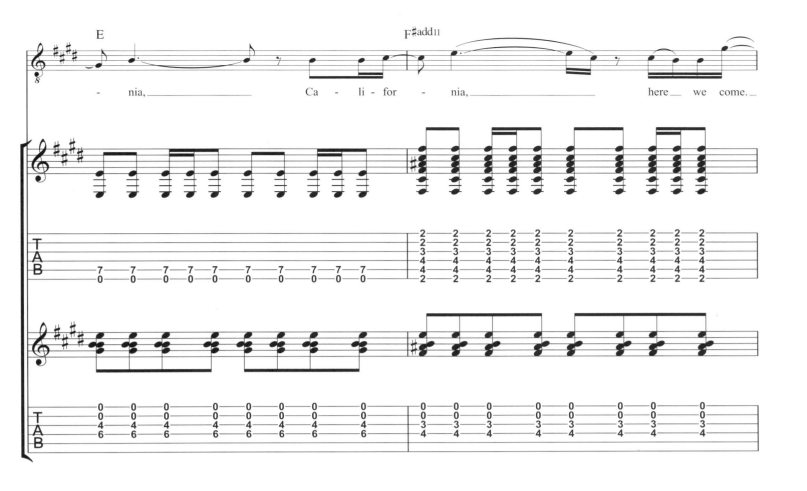

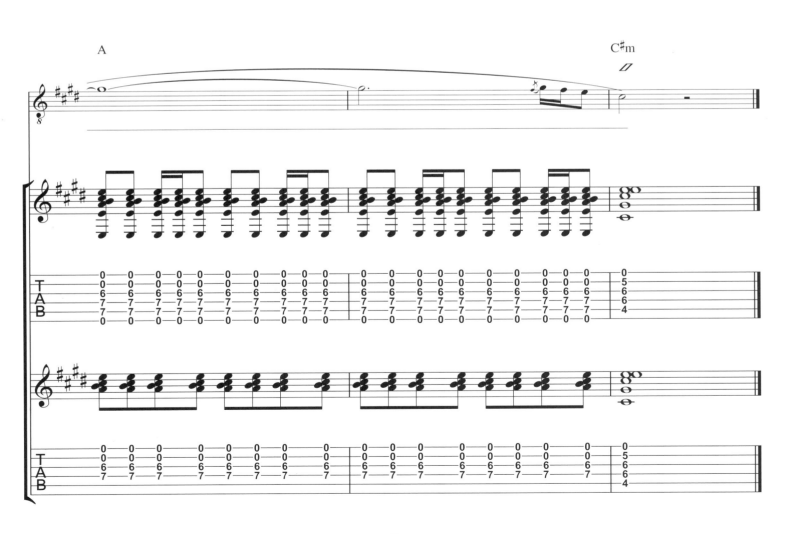

CAN'T STAND ME NOW

WORDS & MUSIC BY PETE DOHERTY, CARL BARÂT & MARK MYERS

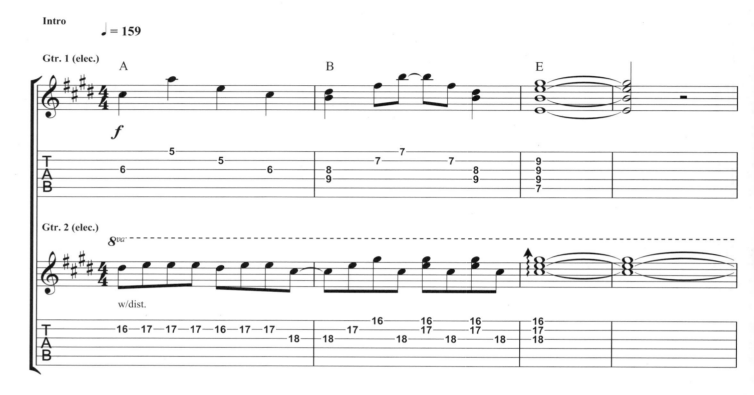

*muted by left hand - finger on fret

let ring...

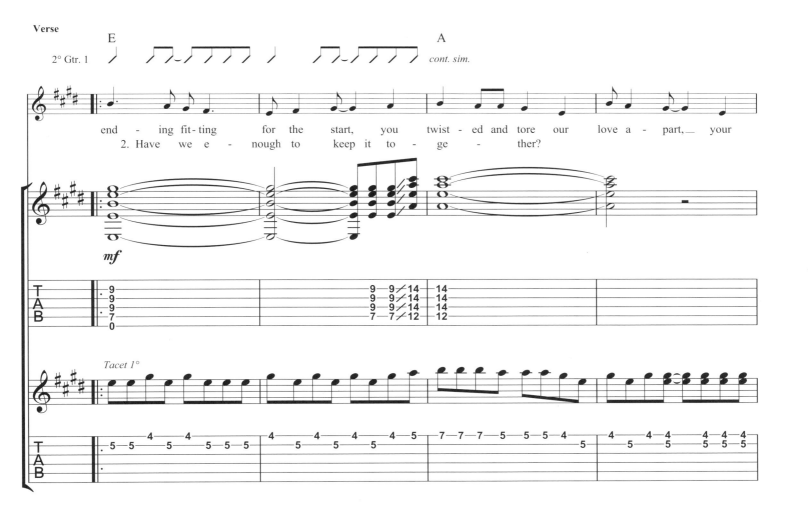

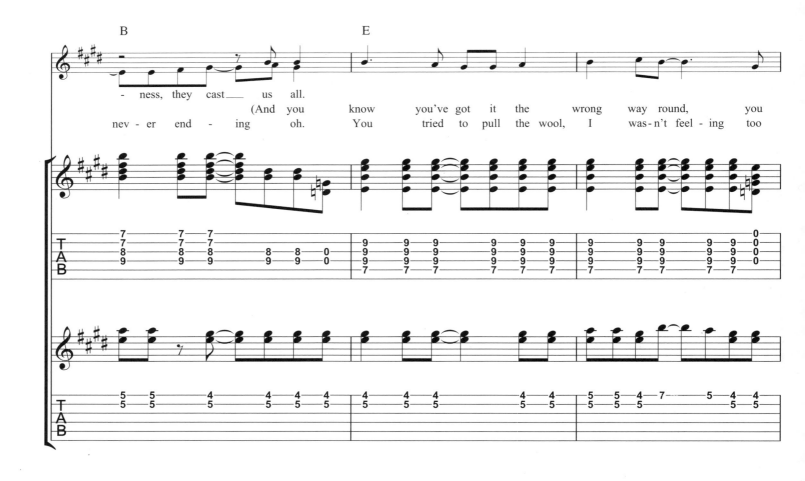

- ness, they cast ___ us all.
(And you know you've got it the wrong way round, you
nev - er end - ing oh. You tried to pull the wool, I was-n't feel - ing too

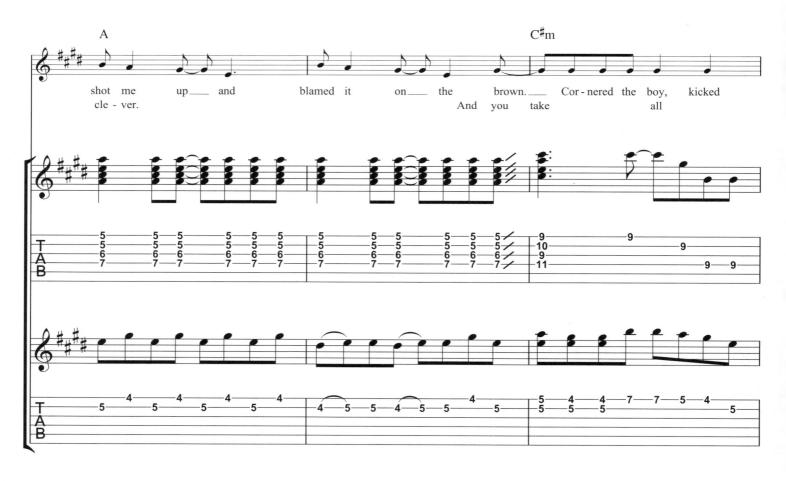

shot me up ___ and blamed it on ___ the brown. ___ Cor - nered the boy, kicked
cle - ver. And you take all

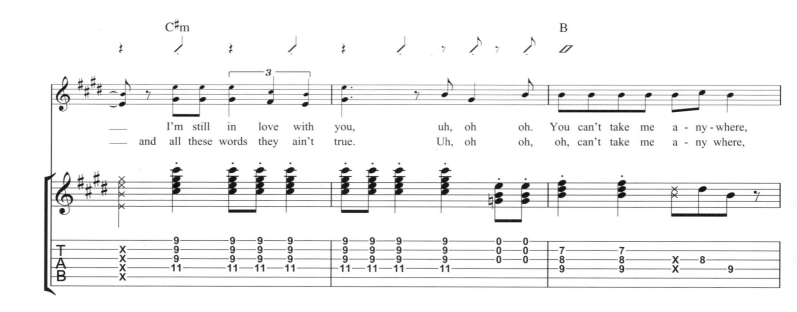

I'm still in love with you, uh, oh oh. You can't take me a-ny-where,
and all these words they ain't true. Uh, oh oh, oh, can't take me a-ny where,

I'll take you a-ny-where, you can't take me a-ny-where, I can't take you a-ny-where,
I can't take you a-ny where, you can't take me a-ny where I won't take you a-ny where,

I'll take you a-ny-where you wan-na go. Oh, you can't stand me, no

cont. in stave

Gtr. 1 cont. in slashes

50

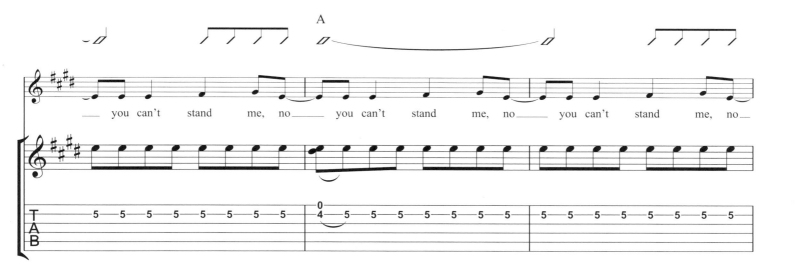

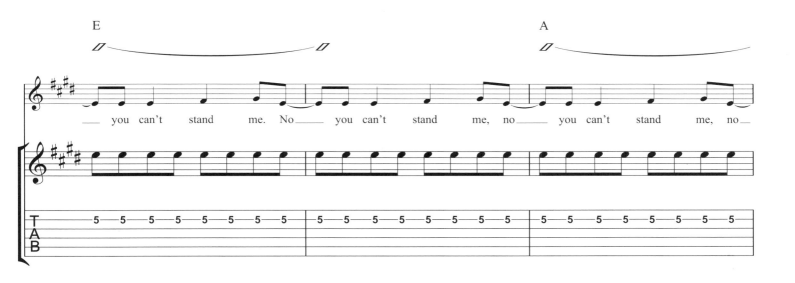

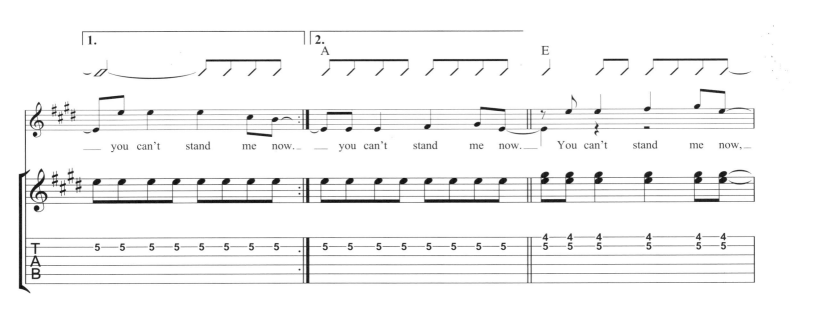

THE END OF THE WORLD

WORDS & MUSIC BY ROBERT SMITH, SIMON GALLUP, PERRY BAMONTE & ROGER O'DONNELL

All Gtrs.

6 = D	3 = F
5 = G	2 = A
4 = C	1 = D

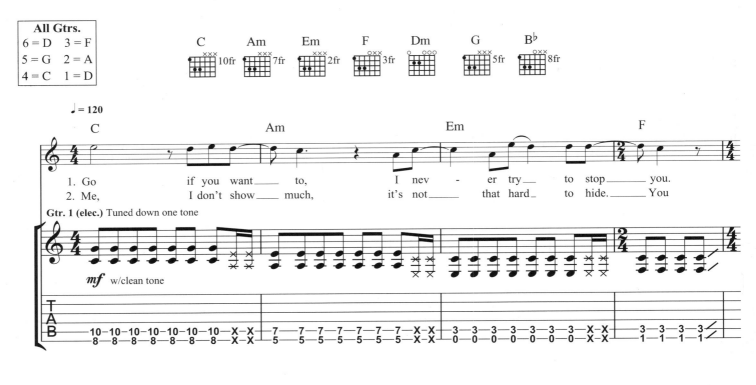

1. Go if you want to, I nev-er try to stop you.
2. Me, I don't show much, it's not that hard to hide. You

Gtr. 1 (elec.) Tuned down one tone

_mf_ w/clean tone

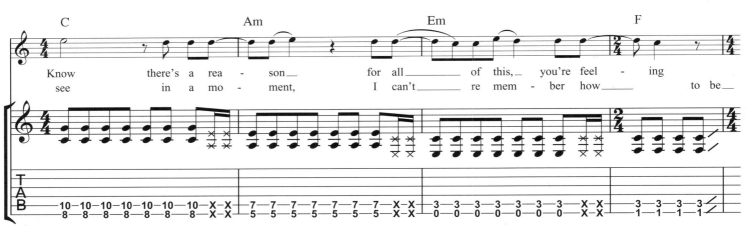

Know there's a rea-son for all of this, you're feel-ing
see in a mo-ment, I can't re-mem-ber how to be

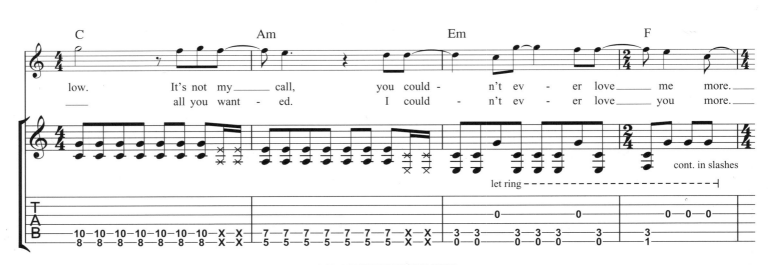

low. It's not my call, you could-n't ev-er love me more.
all you want-ed. I could-n't ev-er love you more.

let ring

cont. in slashes

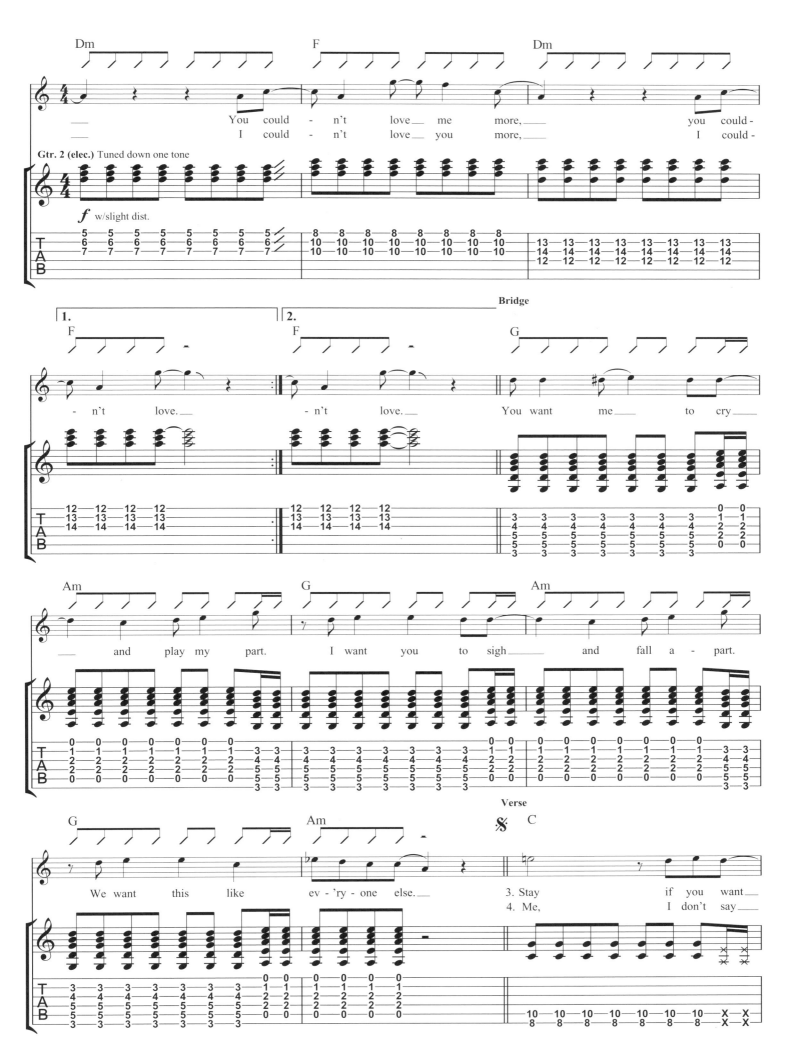

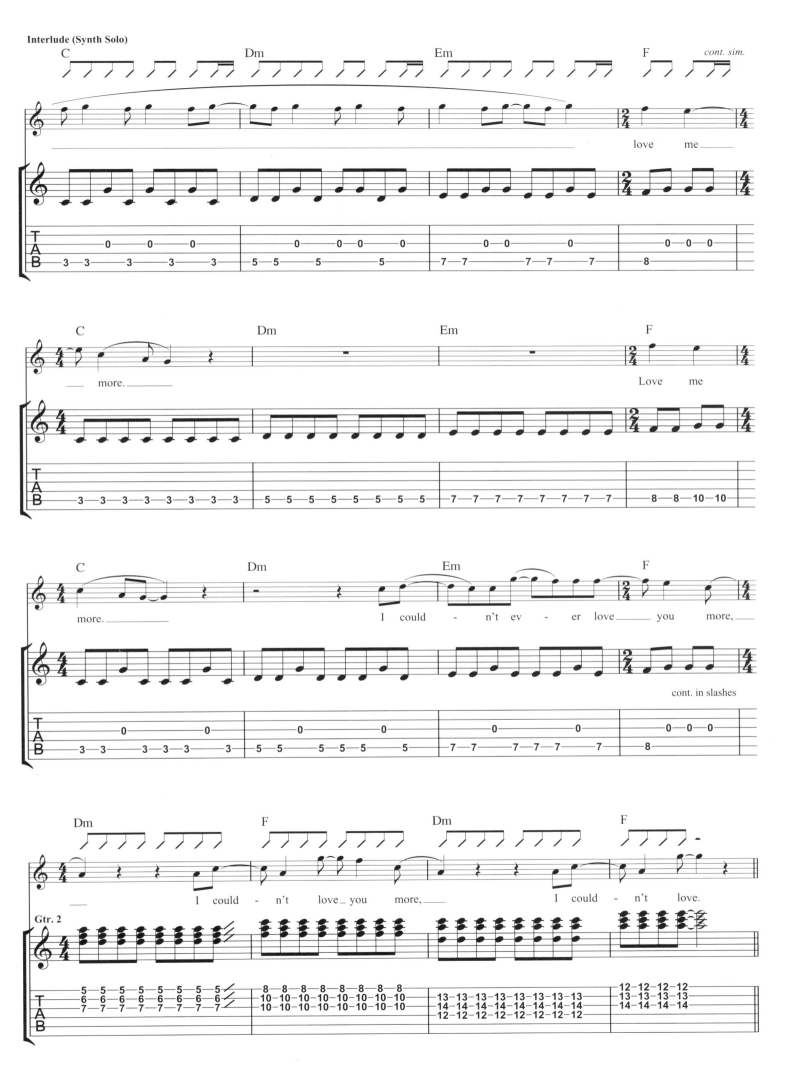

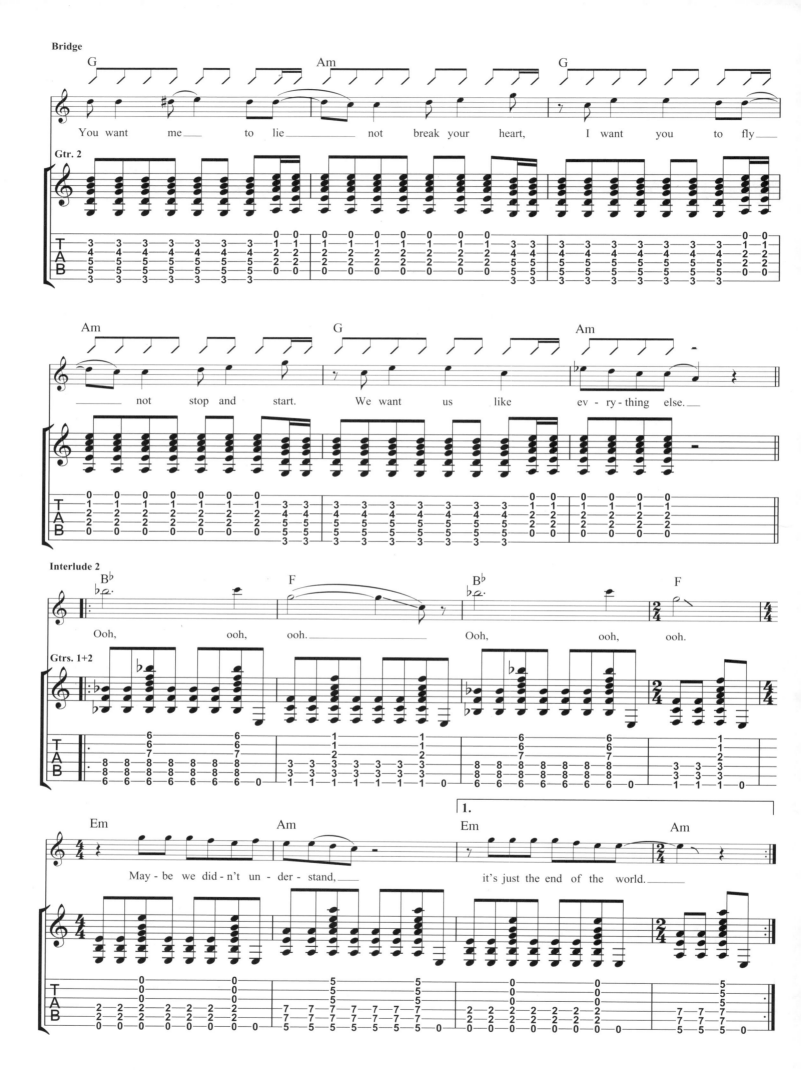

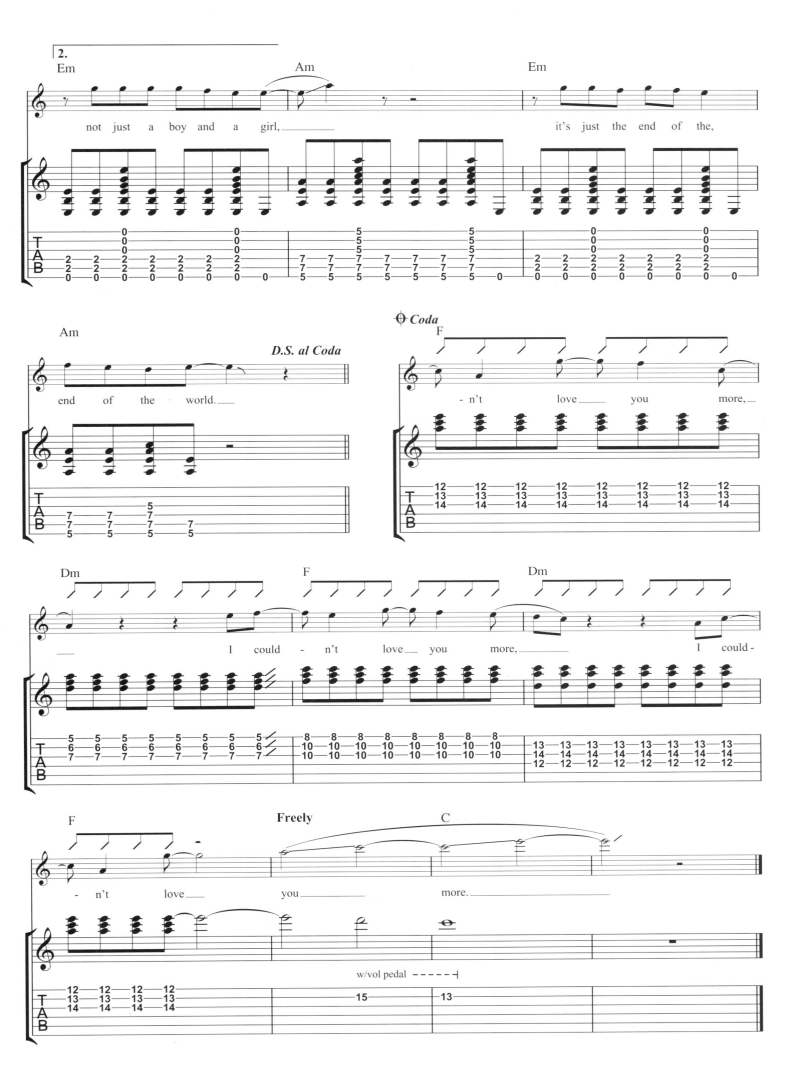

FALL TO PIECES

WORDS & MUSIC BY MATT SORUM, DUFF 'ROSE' McKAGAN, SCOTT WEILAND, DAVID KUSHNER & SAUL HUDSON

Recorded key Db - tune gtrs. down a semitone

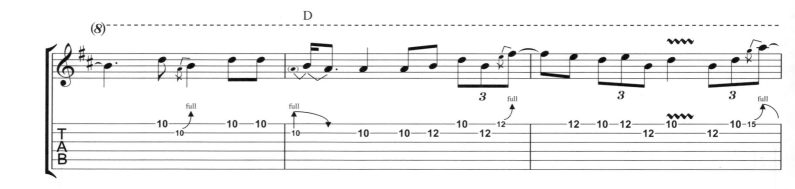

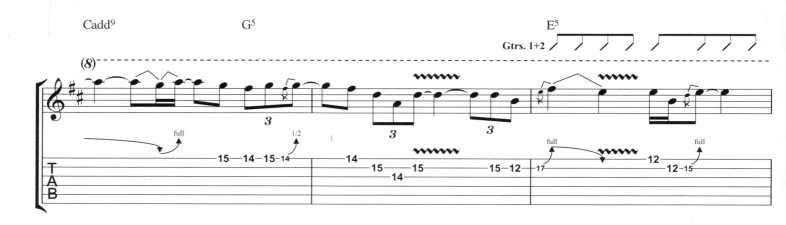

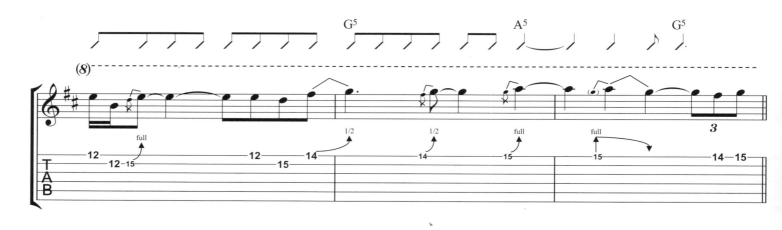

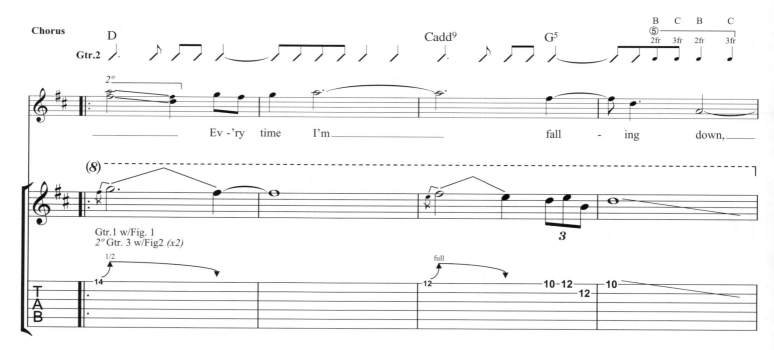

Ev -'ry   time   I'm   fall - ing   down,

66

all a-lone I fall to piec - es.

Ev-'ry time I'm fall - ing down,

all a-lone I fall to piec - es.

to piec - es.

FORGET HER

WORDS & MUSIC BY JEFF BUCKLEY

and all____ the noise has died a - way.____
drop - ping her pet - als in vain, I know.____

I walk____ the streets to stop my weep - ing,____ 'cos she'll nev - er change her
All full of wine, the world be - fore____ her____ was so - ber____ with

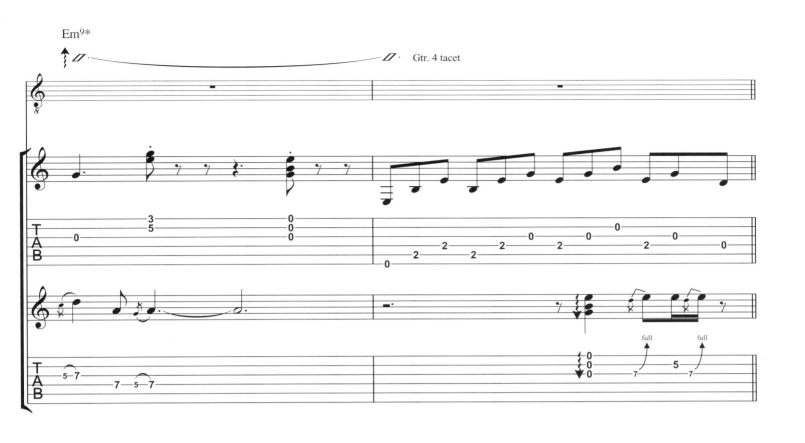

Gtr. 4 tacet

Gtr. solo

Fadd9/A

Gtr. 2
(acous.)

rhy. cont. sim.

Cadd9

G6/B

Em7

Well   my

rake - - - -

73

Bridge

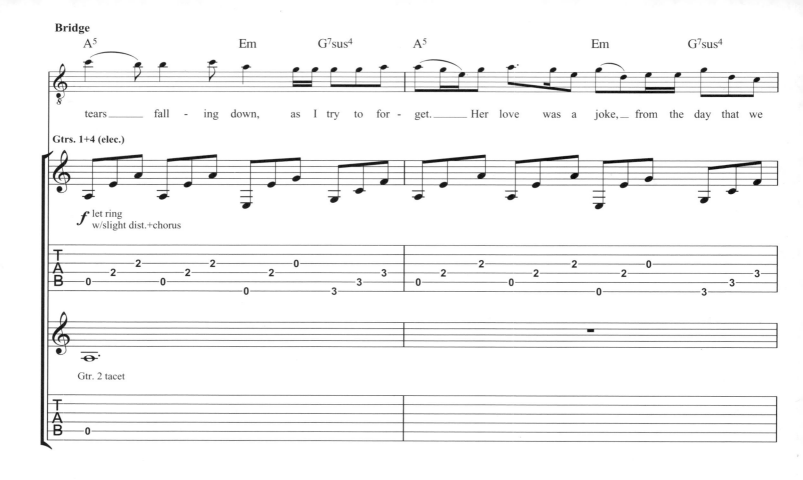

tears _____ fall - ing down, as I try to for - get. _____ Her love was a joke, _____ from the day that we

Gtrs. 1+4 (elec.)

f let ring
w/slight dist.+chorus

Gtr. 2 tacet

met. _____ All of the words, all of the men. All of my pain _____ when I think _ back to

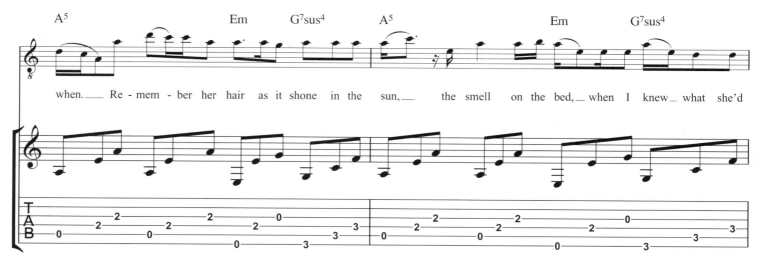

when. _____ Re - mem - ber her hair as it shone in the sun, _____ the smell on the bed, _ when I knew _ what she'd

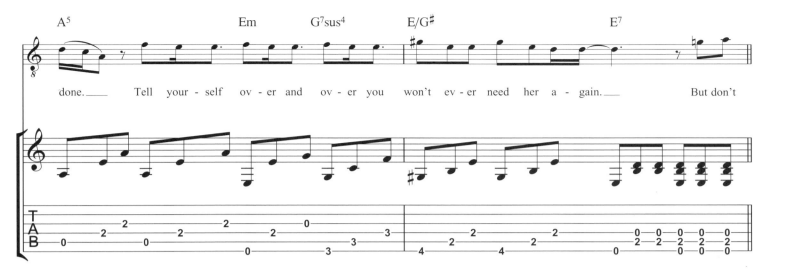

done.___ Tell your-self ov-er and ov-er you won't ev-er need her a-gain.___ But don't

Chorus

Gtr. 2 (acous.)

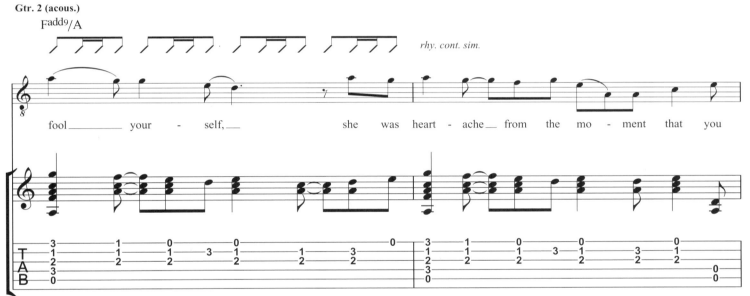

fool___ your-self,___ she was heart-ache___ from the mo-ment that you

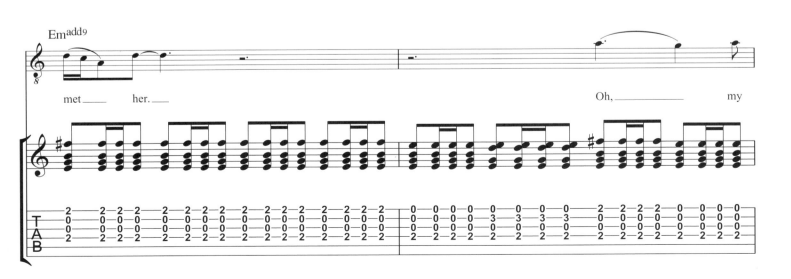

met___ her.___ Oh,_____ my

GOLDEN TOUCH

WORDS & MUSIC BY Johnny Borrell

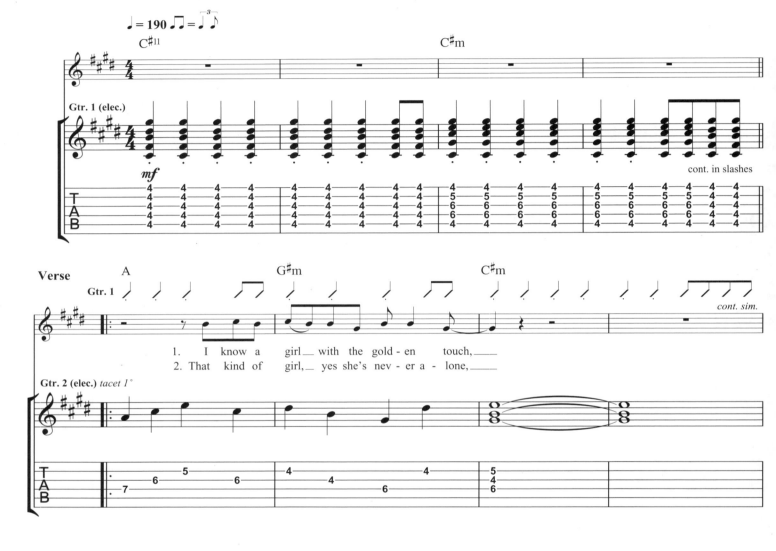

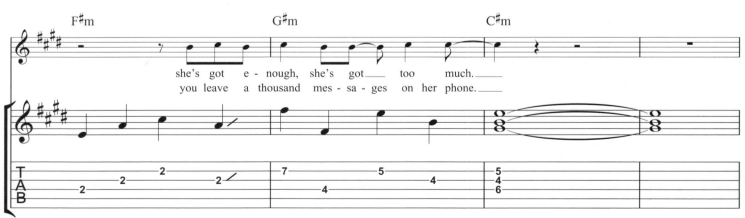

Verse

1. I know a girl with the gold-en touch,
2. That kind of girl, yes she's nev-er a - lone,

she's got e - nough, she's got too much.
you leave a thousand mes-sa-ges on her phone.

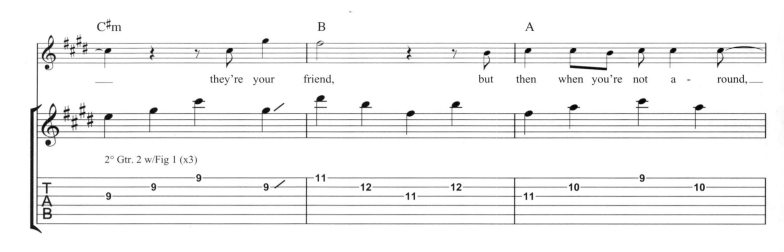

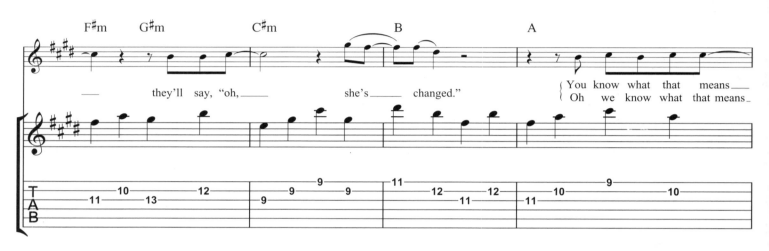

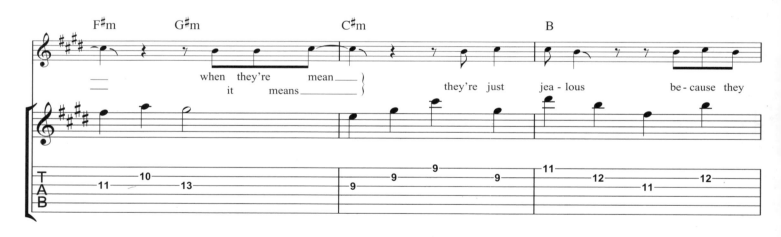

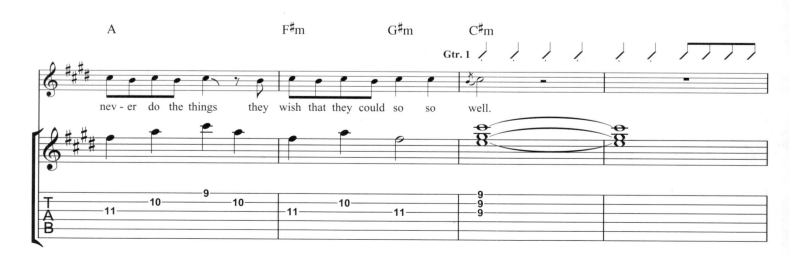

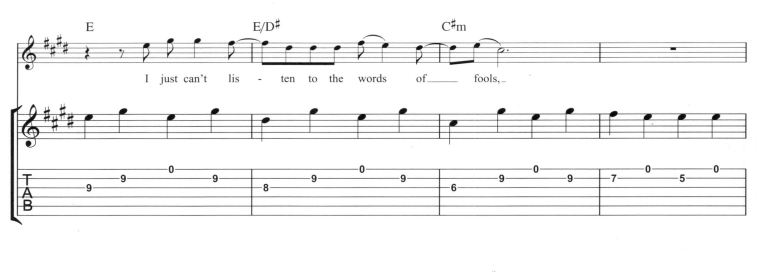

I just can't lis - ten to the words of ___ fools, ___

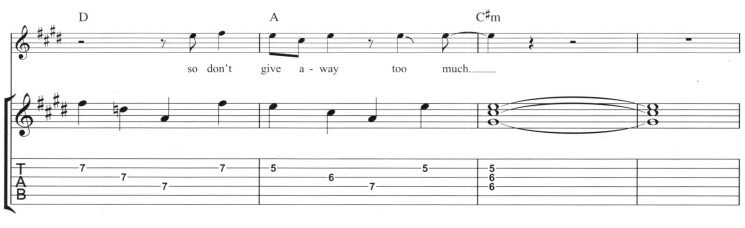

so don't give a - way too much. ___

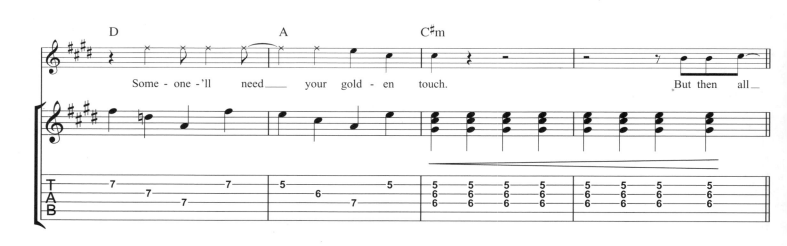

Some - one -'ll need ___ your gold - en touch. But then all ___

Chorus

___ they know ___ is how to put you down. ___ When you're there, ___

GRAVITY

WORDS & MUSIC BY GUY BERRYMAN, CHRIS MARTIN, JON BUCKLAND & WILL CHAMPION

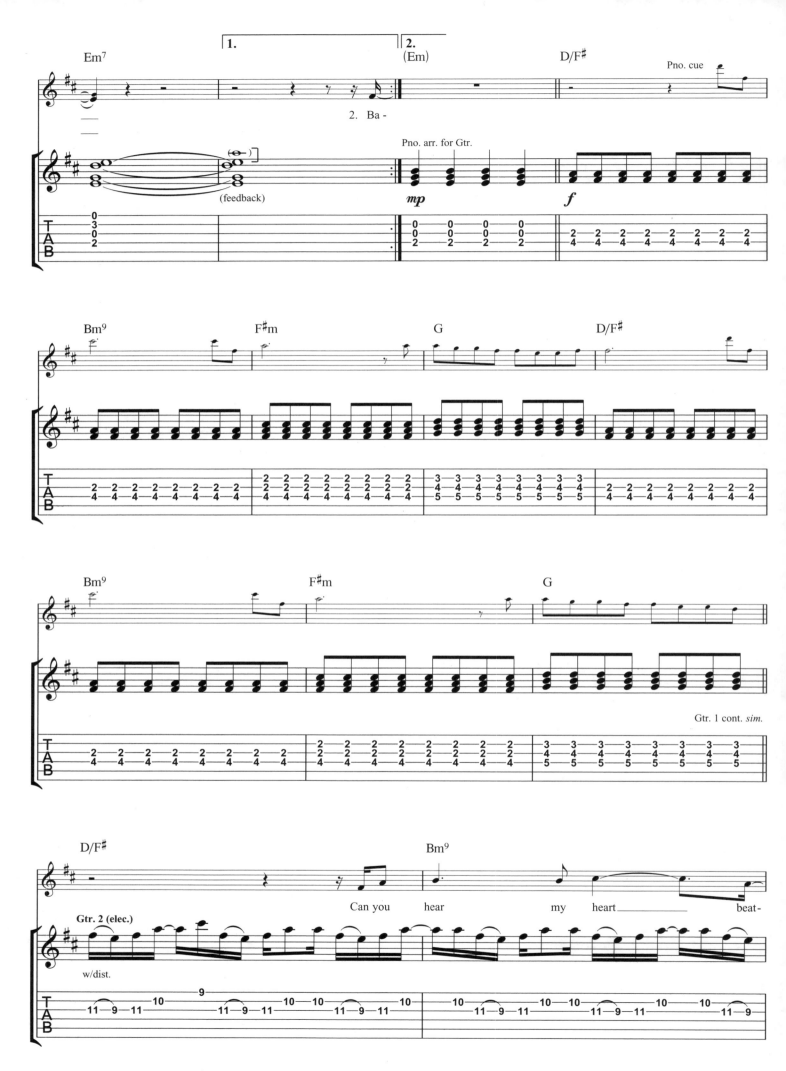

THE LETTER

WORDS & MUSIC BY POLLY JEAN HARVEY

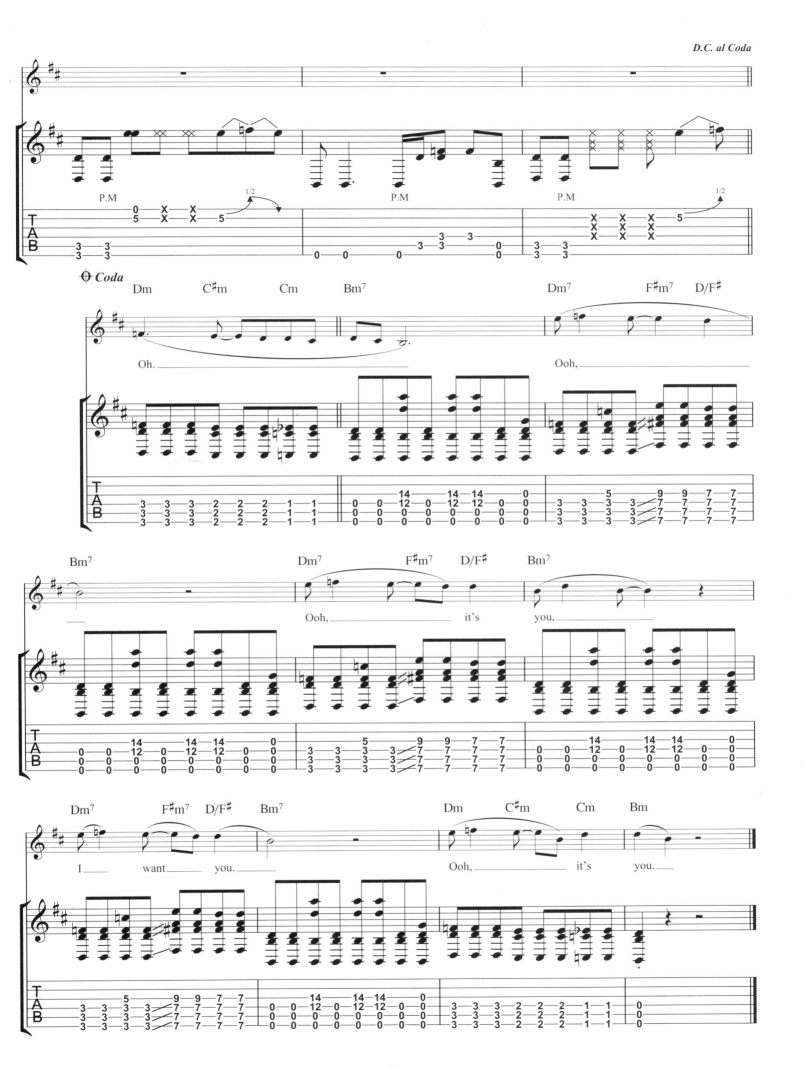

MAPS

WORDS & MUSIC BY KAREN O, NICHOLAS ZINNER & BRIAN CHASE

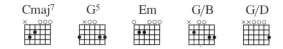

love you like I love you. Wait, they don't love you like I love you. Maps, _____

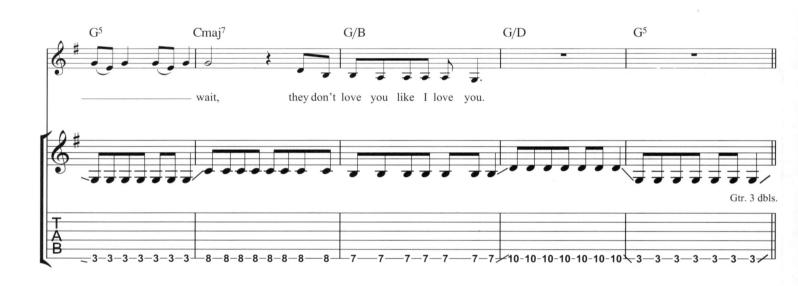

_____ wait, they don't love you like I love you.

Gtr. 3 dbls.

Interlude

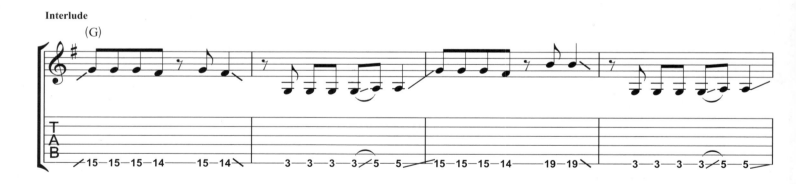

To Coda ⊕

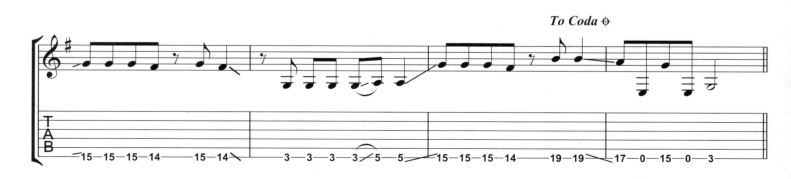

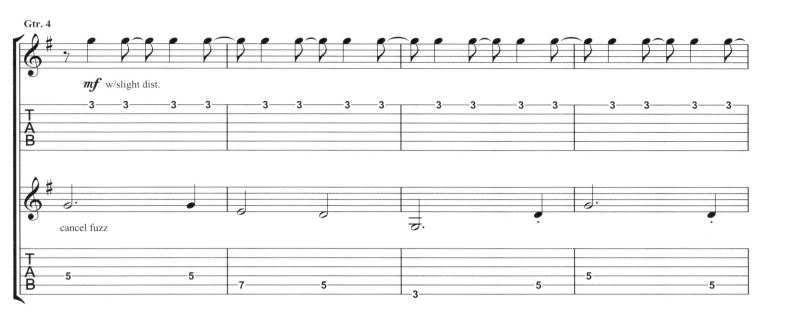

D.S. al Coda

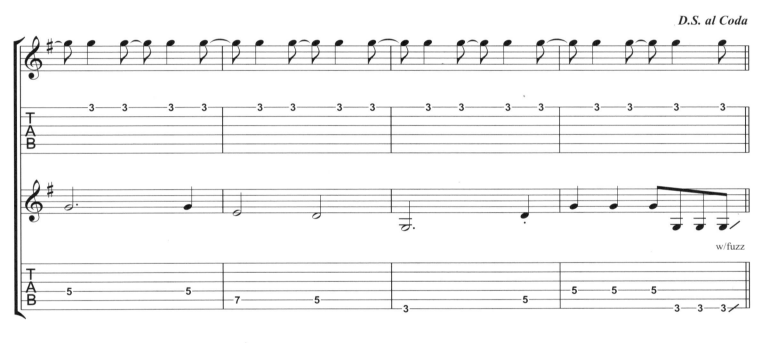

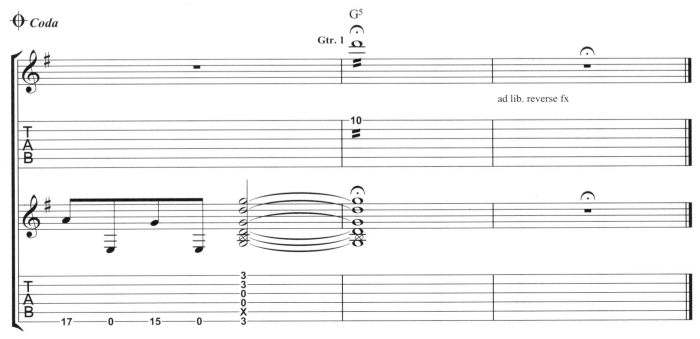

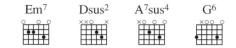

KEEP WHAT YA GOT

WORDS & MUSIC BY IAN BROWN & NOEL GALLAGHER

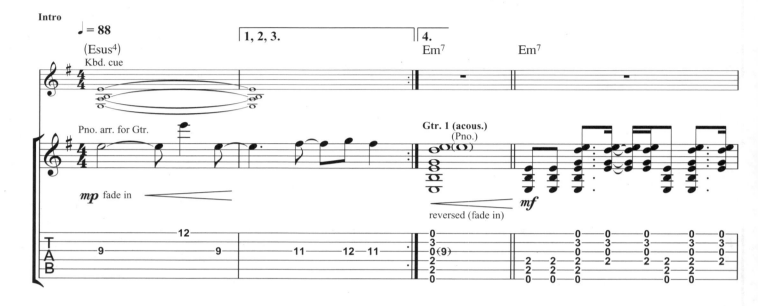

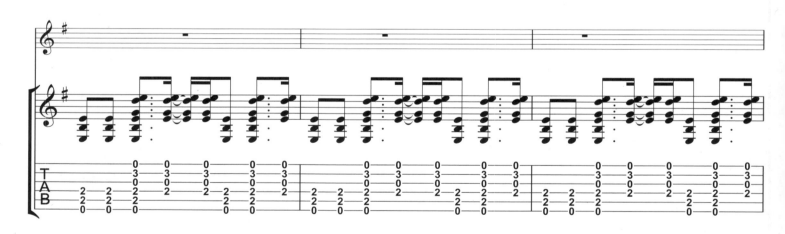

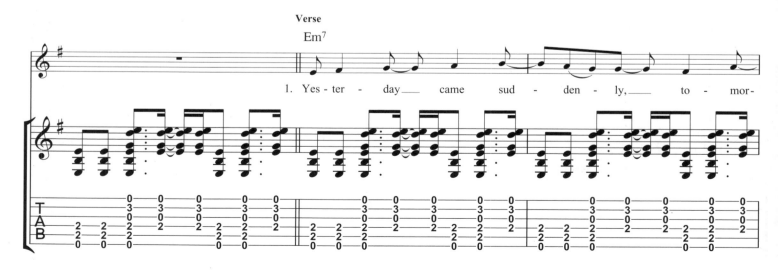

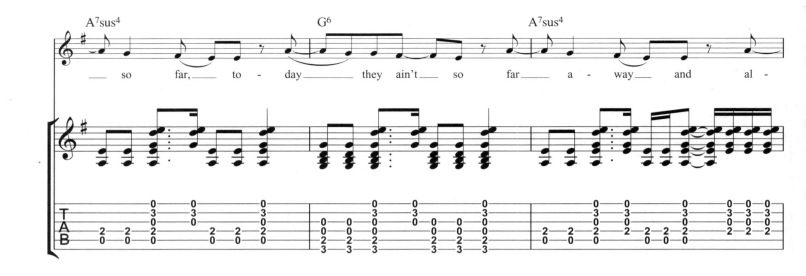

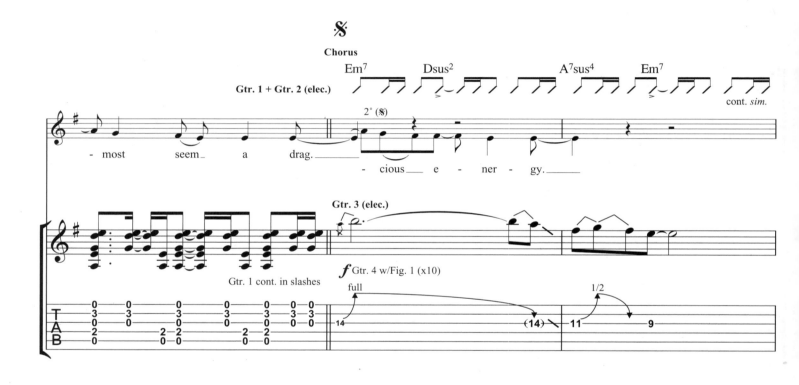

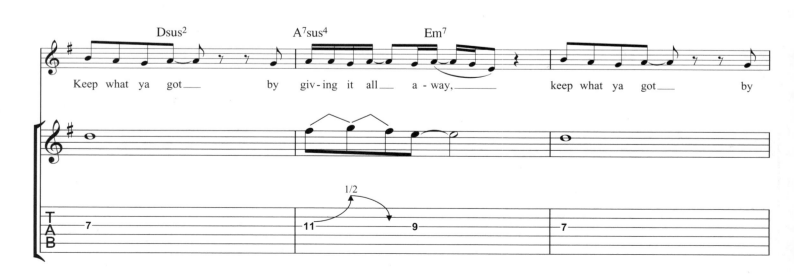

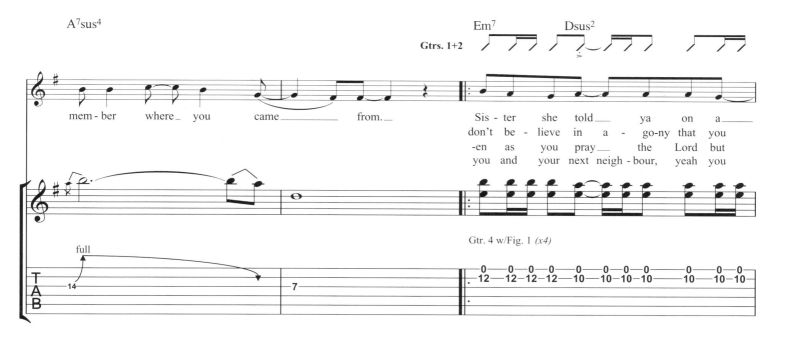

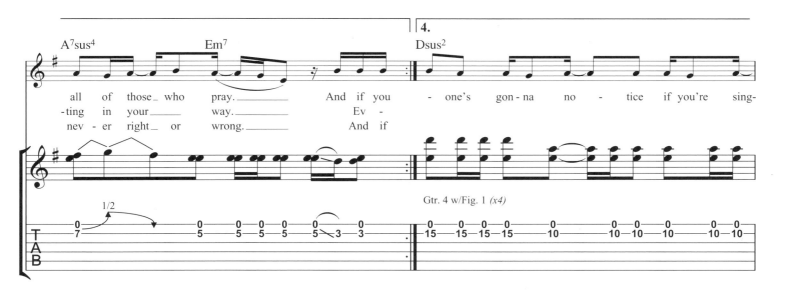

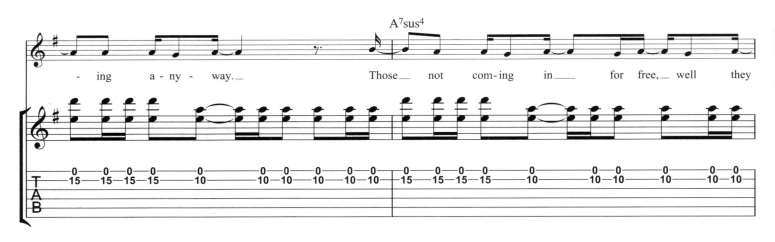

-ing a-ny - way.___ Those___ not com - ing in___ for free,___ well they

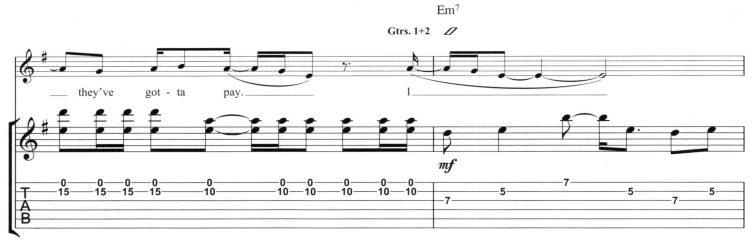

___ they've got - ta pay.___ I

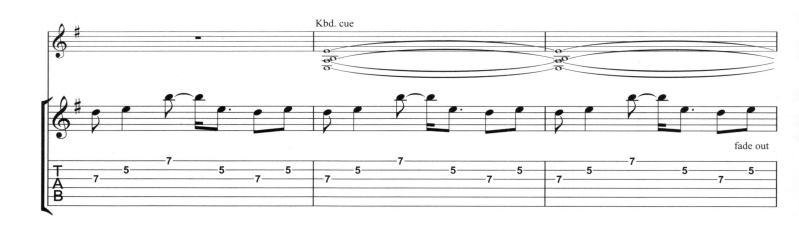

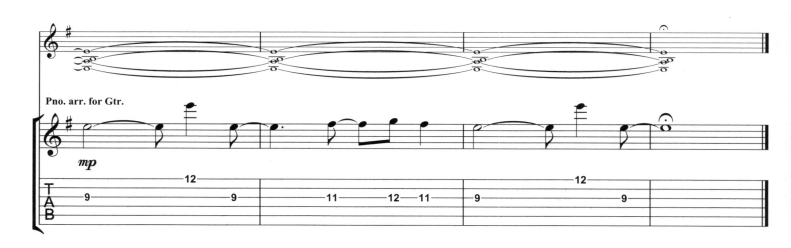

MICHAEL

WORDS & MUSIC BY ALEXANDER KAPRANOS & NICHOLAS MCCARTHY

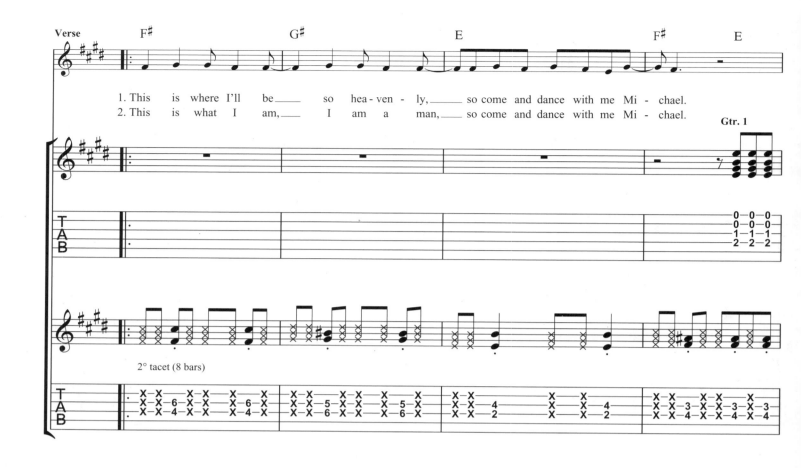

1. This is where I'll be___ so hea - ven - ly,___ so come and dance with me Mi - chael.
2. This is what I am,___ I am a man,___ so come and dance with me Mi - chael.

2° tacet (8 bars)

So se - xy, I'm se - xy,_____ so come and dance with me Mi - chael.
So strong now, it's strong now,_____ so come and dance with me Mi - chael.

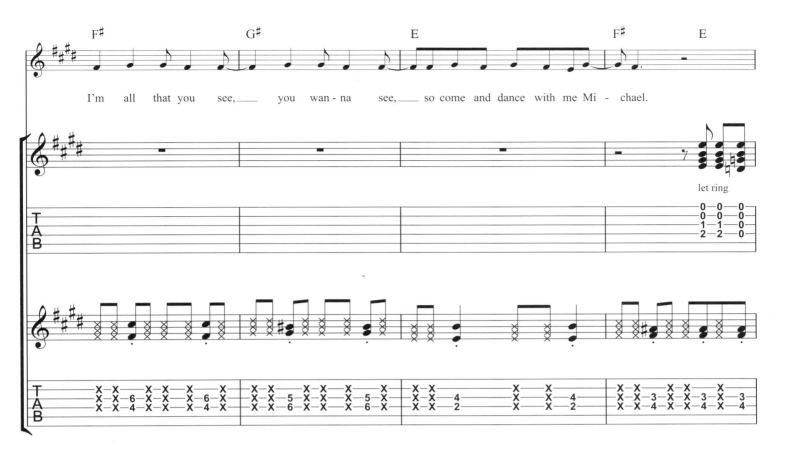

I'm all that you see,___ you wan - na see,___ so come and dance with me Mi - chael.

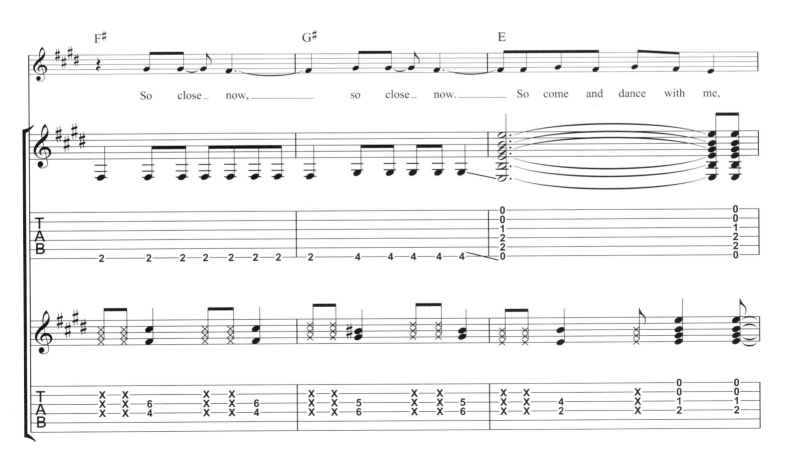

So close___ now,_____ so close___ now._____ So come and dance with me,

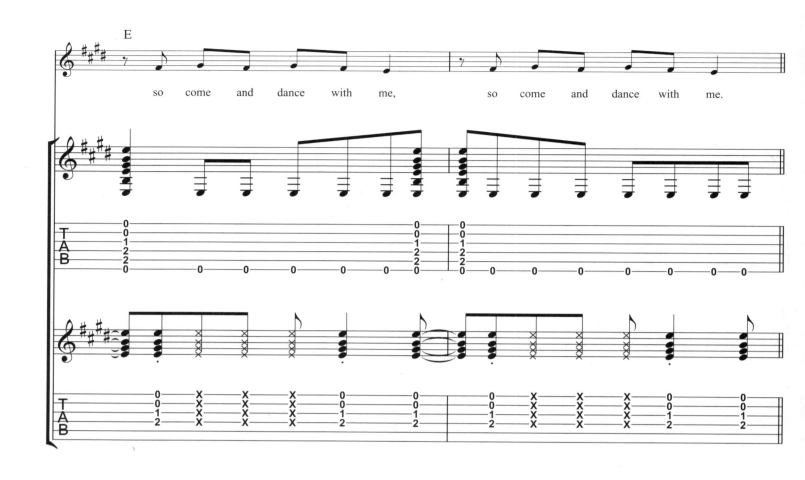

so come and dance with me, so come and dance with me.

Chorus

1. 2. Mi - chael, you're the boy____ with all the lea - ther hips, stick - y hair, stick - y hips, stub -

3. Mi - chael you're the on - ly one I'd ev - er want, on - ly one I'd ev - er want, on -

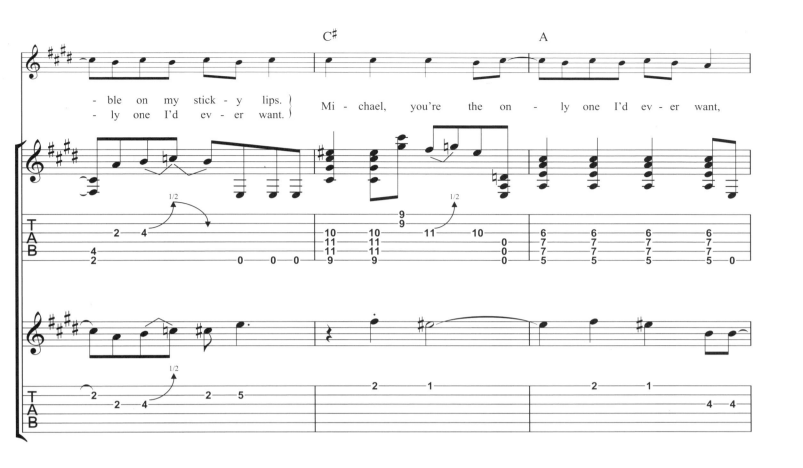

-ble on my stick-y lips.
-ly one I'd ev-er want.

Mi-chael, you're the on-ly one I'd ev-er want,

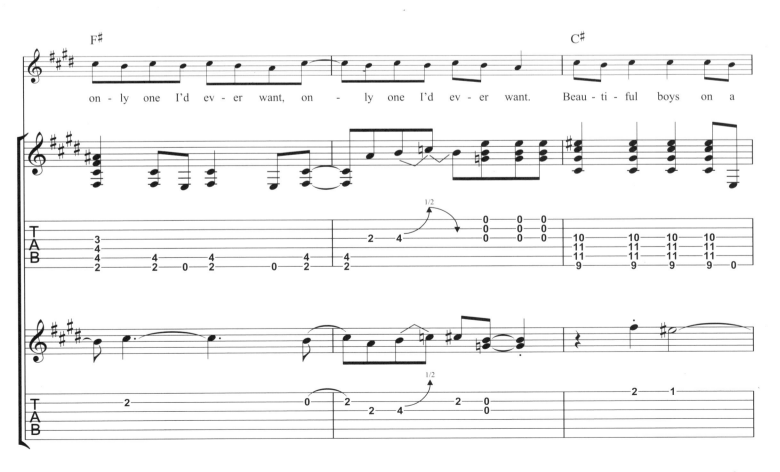

on-ly one I'd ev-er want, on-ly one I'd ev-er want.

Beau-ti-ful boys on a

beau - ti - ful dance - floor,   Mi - chael, you're danc - ing like a beau - ti - ful   dance - whore.

Mi - chael wait - ing on a silv - er plat - ter now,____   and no - thing mat - ters now.

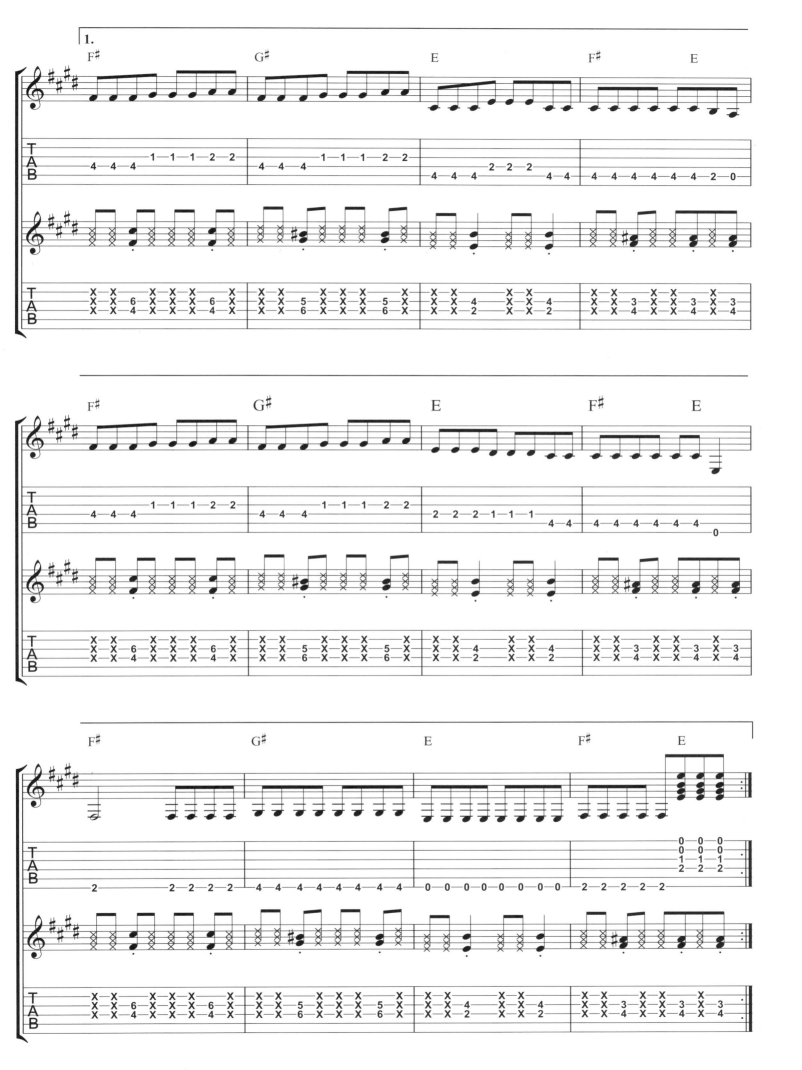

silver plat-ter now, no-thing mat-ters now,

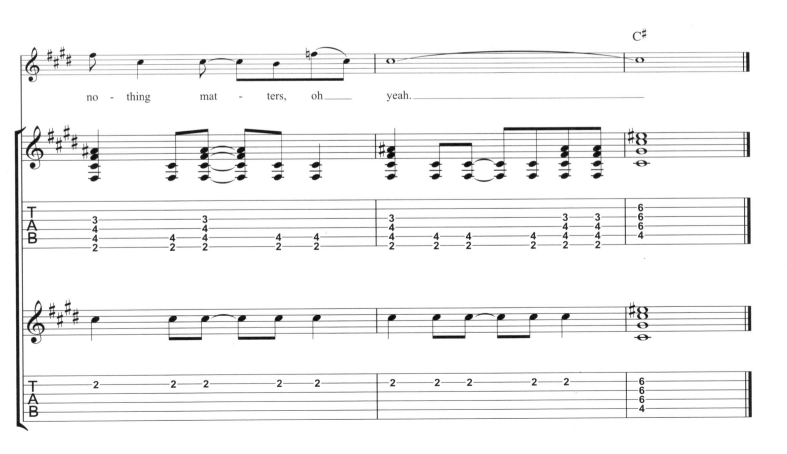

no-thing mat-ters, oh_____ yeah._____

ORPHEUS

WORDS & MUSIC BY TIM WHEELER

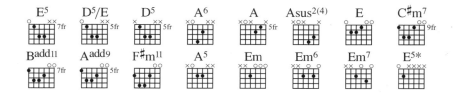

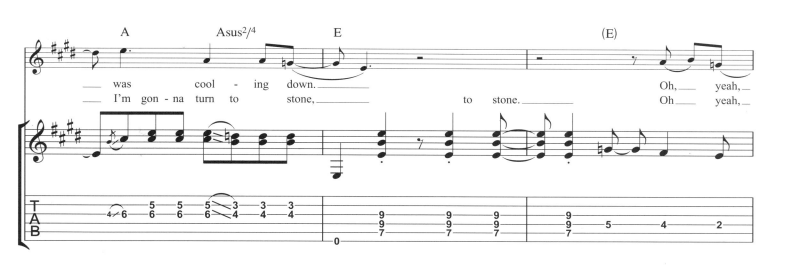

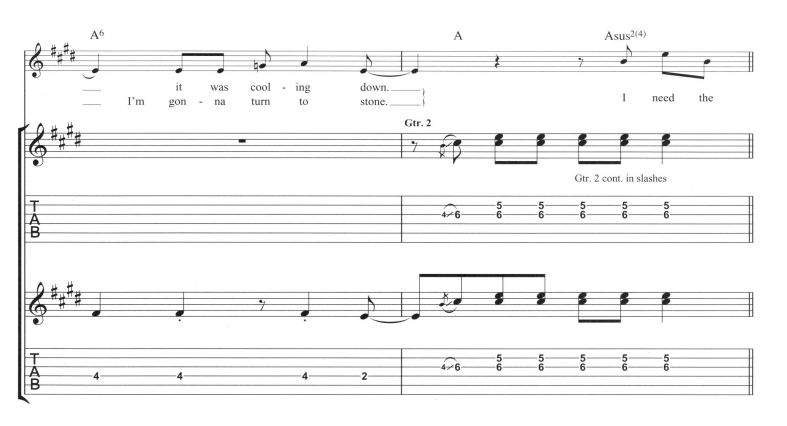

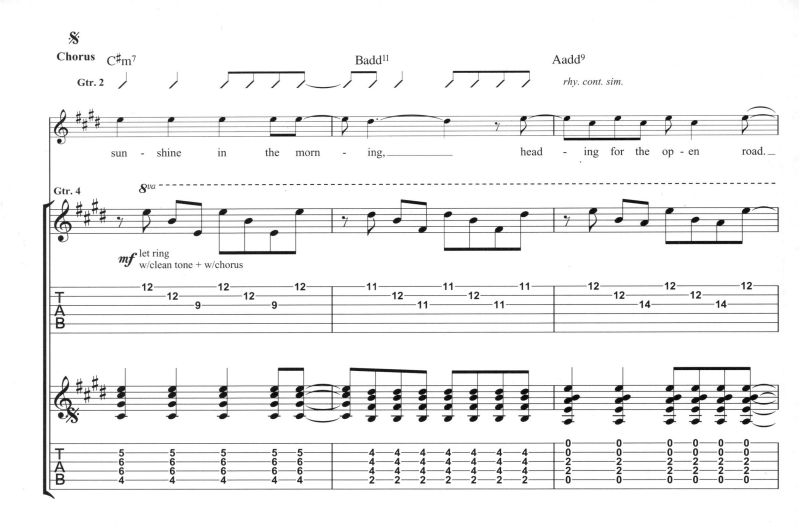

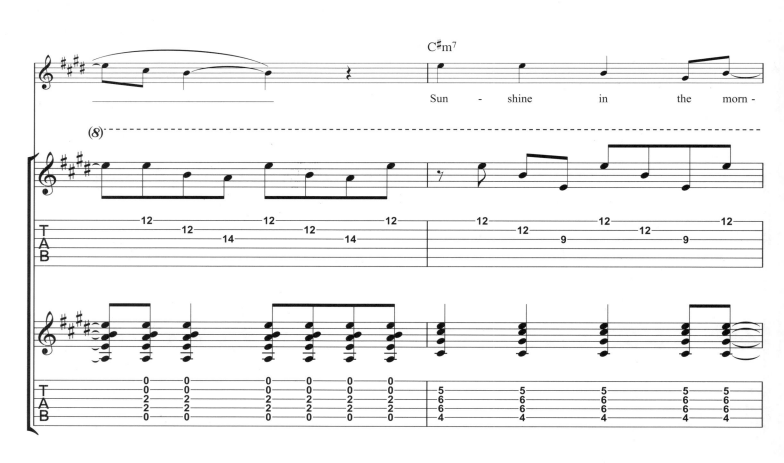

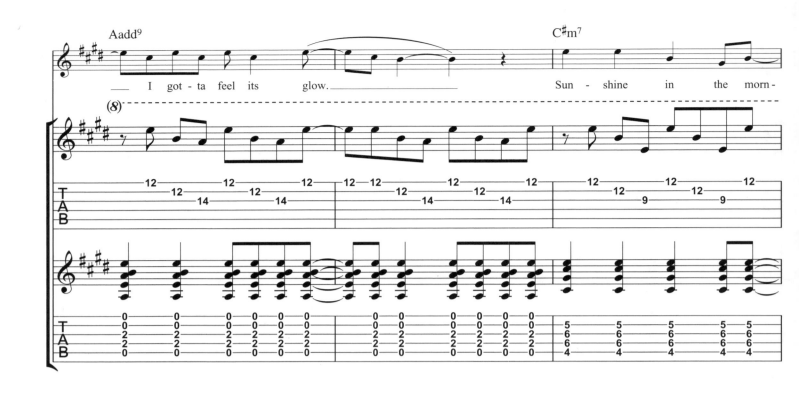

_I gotta feel its glow.___ Sunshine in the morn-_

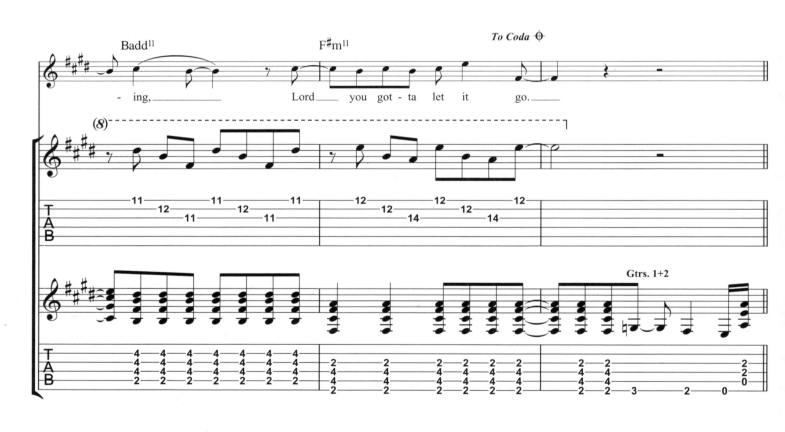

_-ing,___ Lord___ you gotta let it go.____

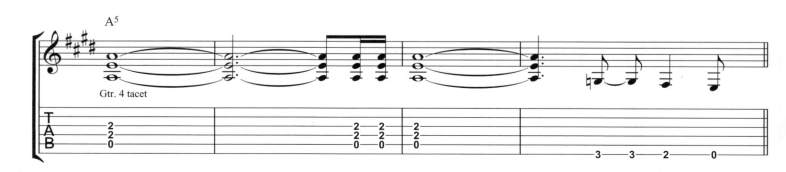

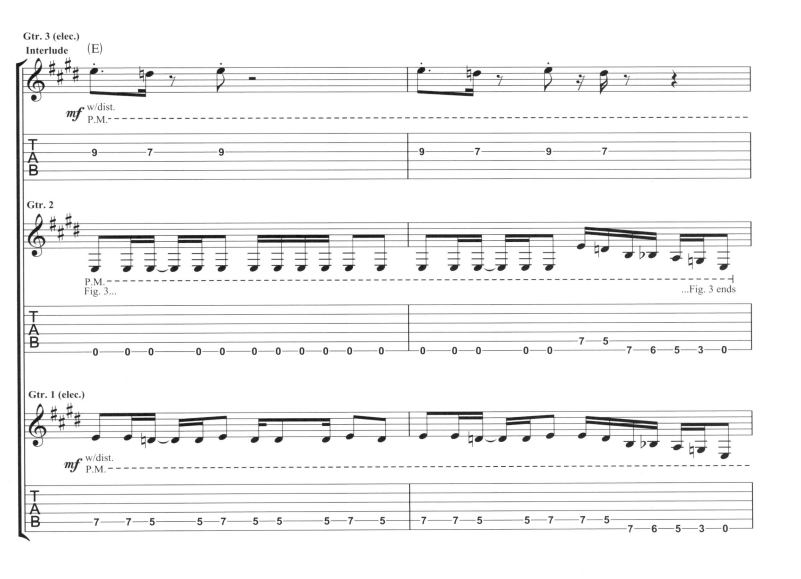

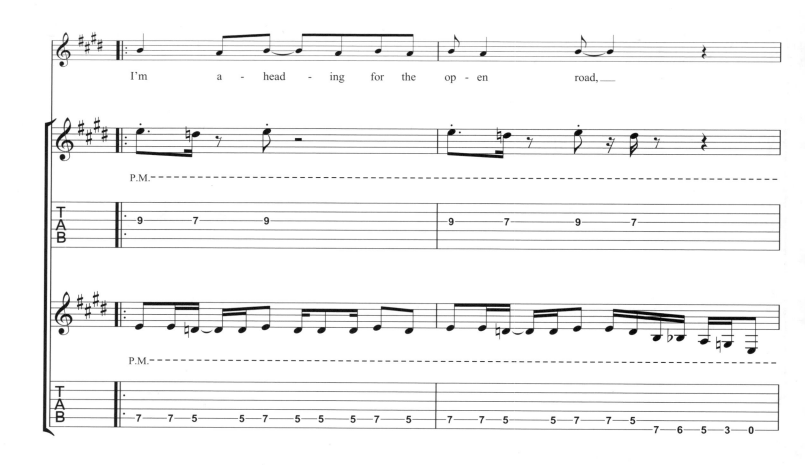

I'm a - head - ing for the op - en road, ___

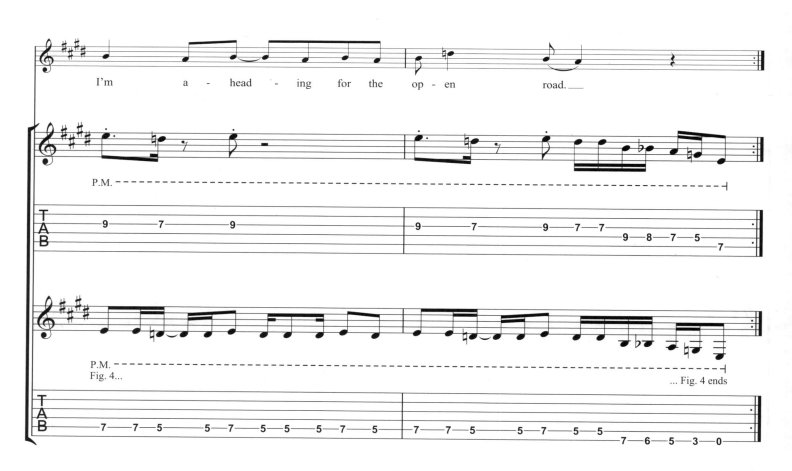

I'm a - head - ing for the op - en road. ___

Fig. 4... ... Fig. 4 ends

123

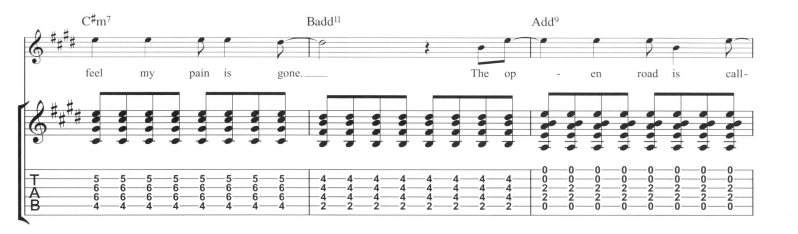

feel my pain is gone._____ The op - en road is call-

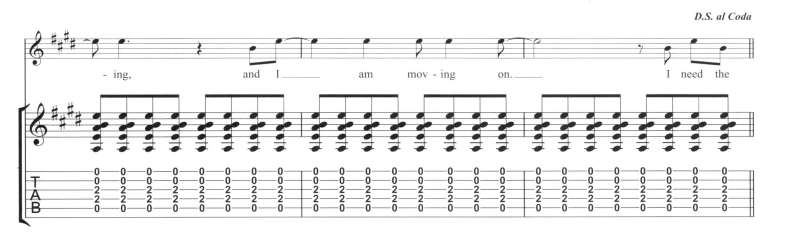

D.S. al Coda

- ing, and I _____ am mov - ing on. _____ I need the

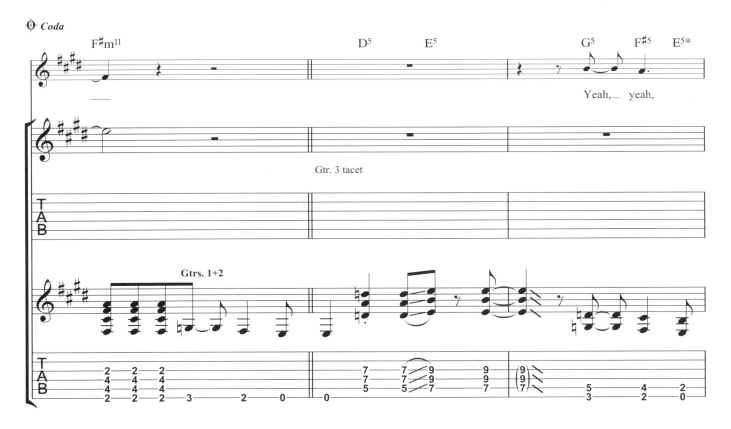

Coda

Yeah, ___ yeah,

Gtr. 3 tacet

Gtrs. 1+2

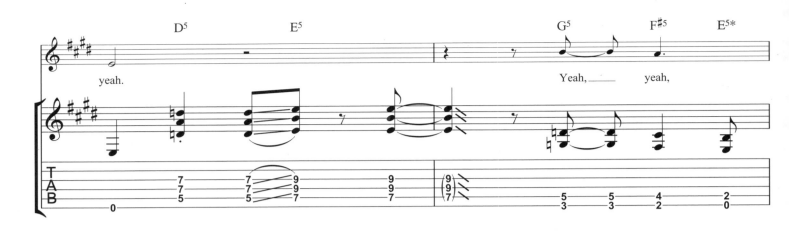

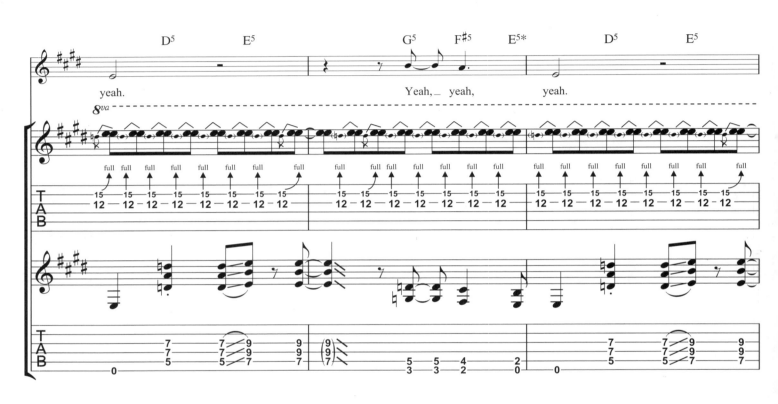

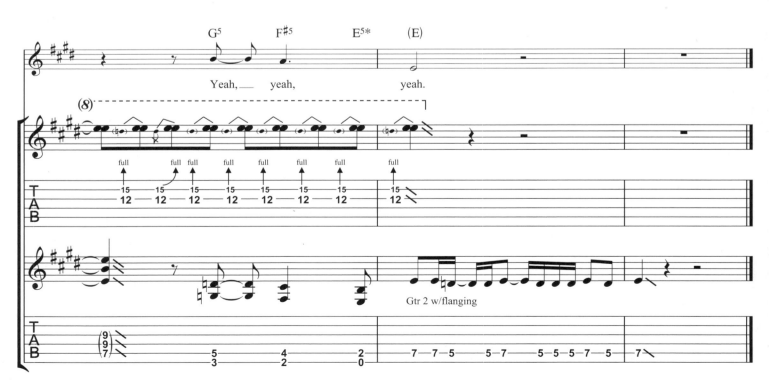

RIDE
WORDS & MUSIC BY CRAIG NICHOLLS

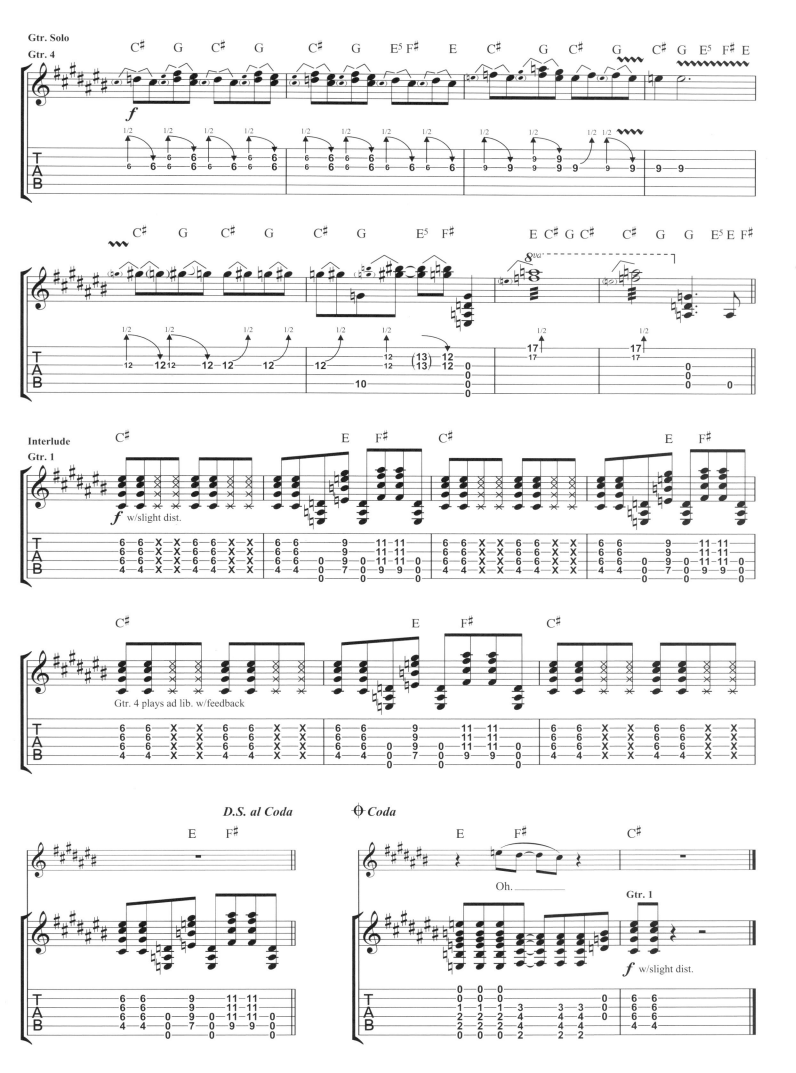

ROLLOVER DJ

WORDS & MUSIC BY NIC CESTER & CAMERON MUNCEY

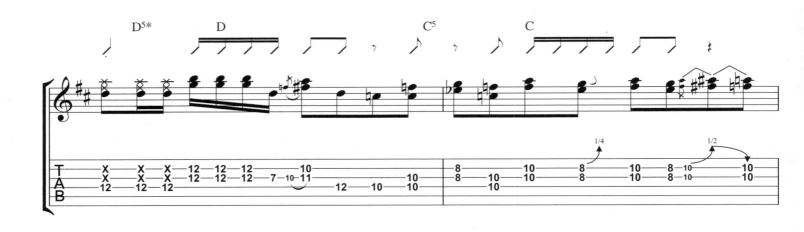
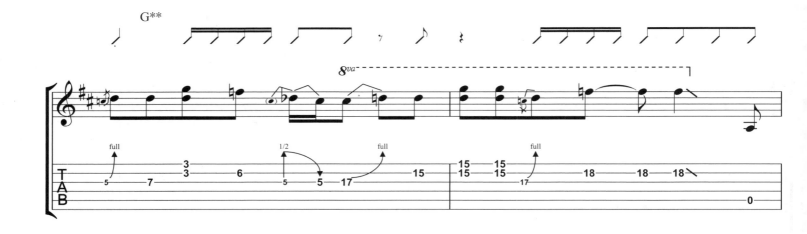
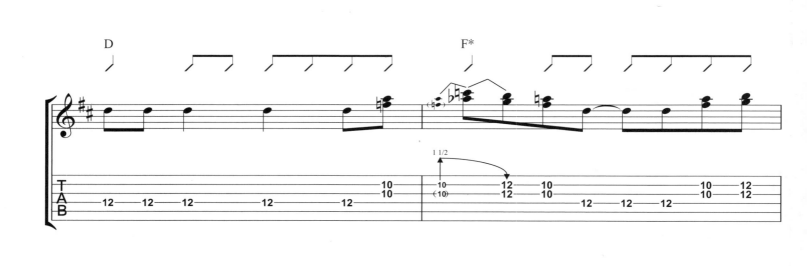
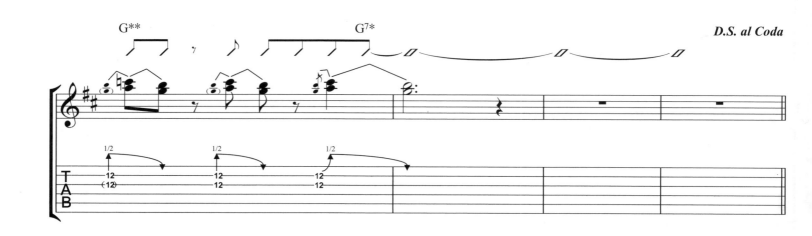

137

SOLITARY MAN
WORDS & MUSIC BY NEIL DIAMOND

139

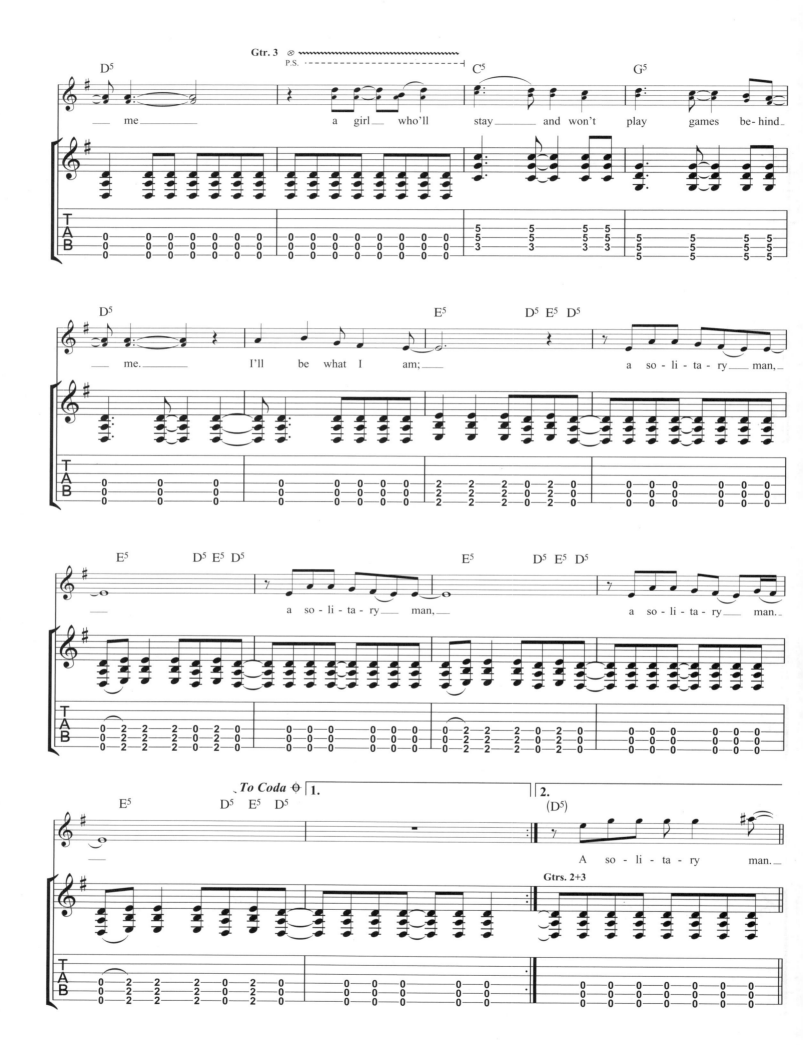

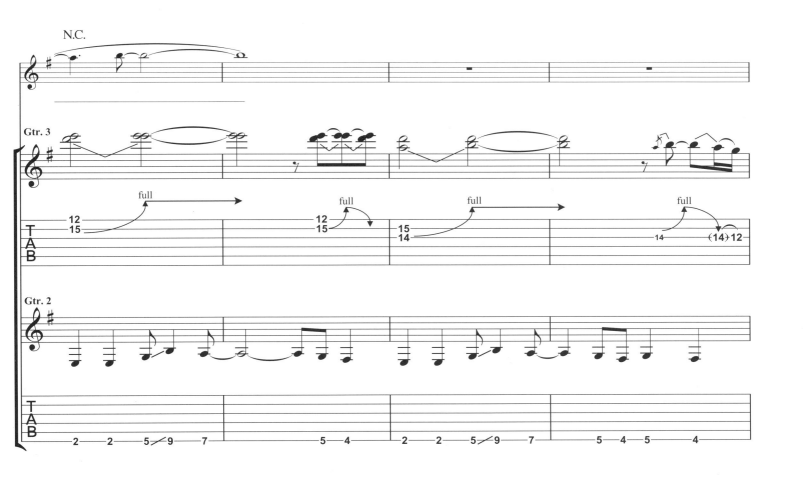

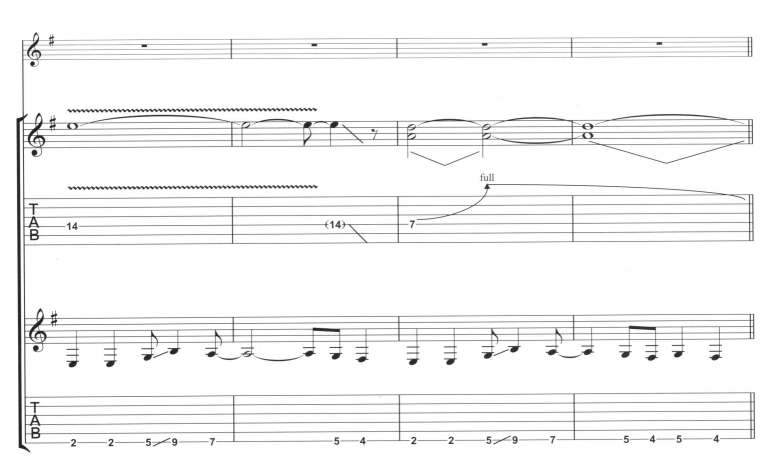

SOMEBODY TOLD ME

WORDS & MUSIC BY BRANDON FLOWERS, DAVE KEUNING, MARK STOERMER & RONNIE VAN NUCCI

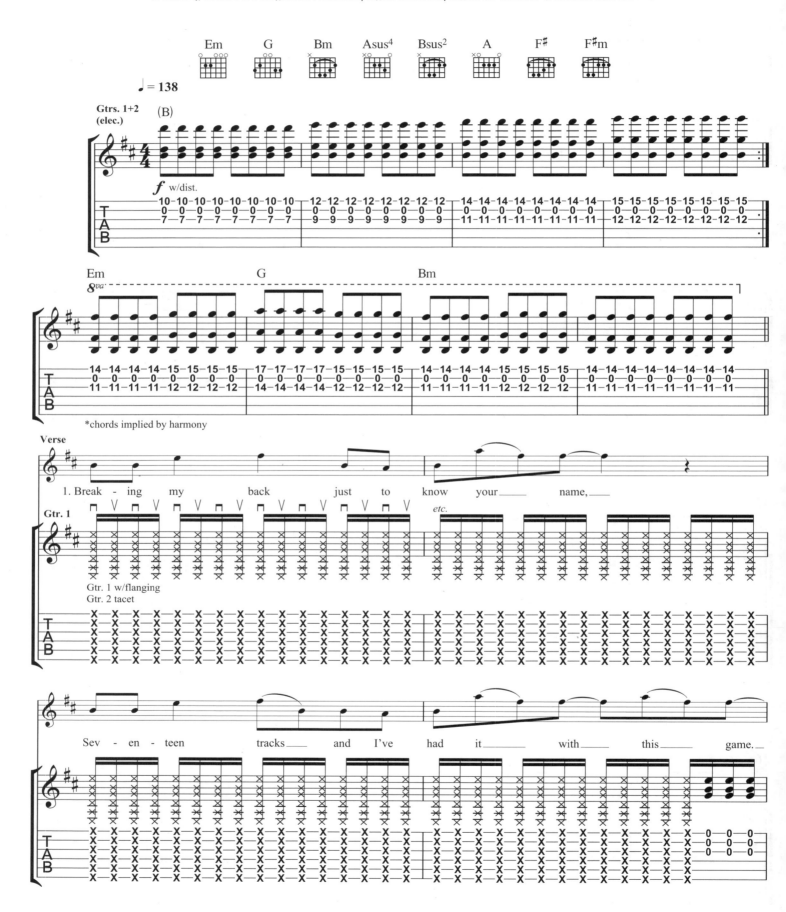

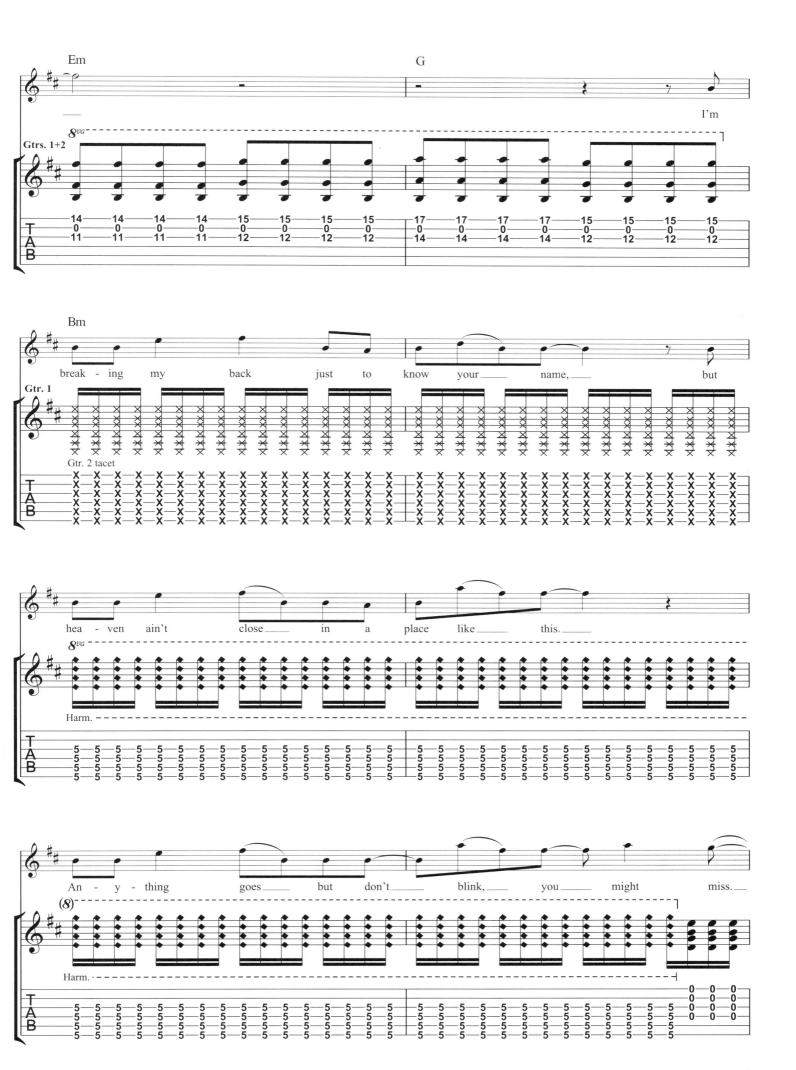

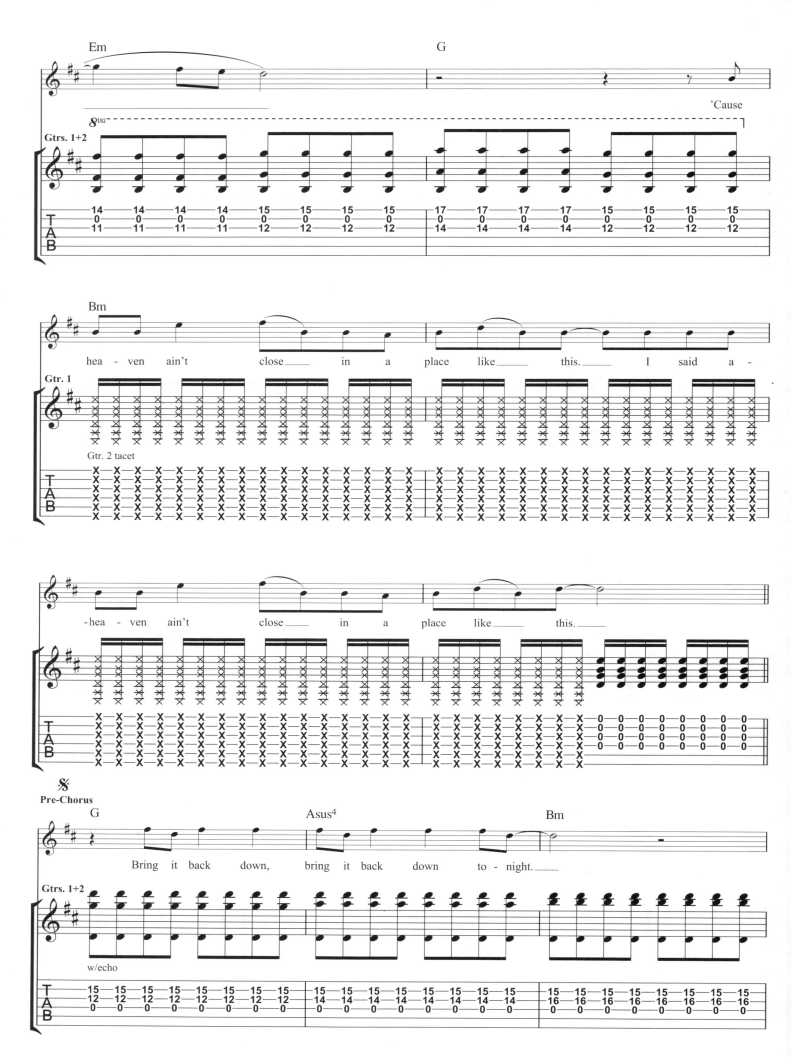

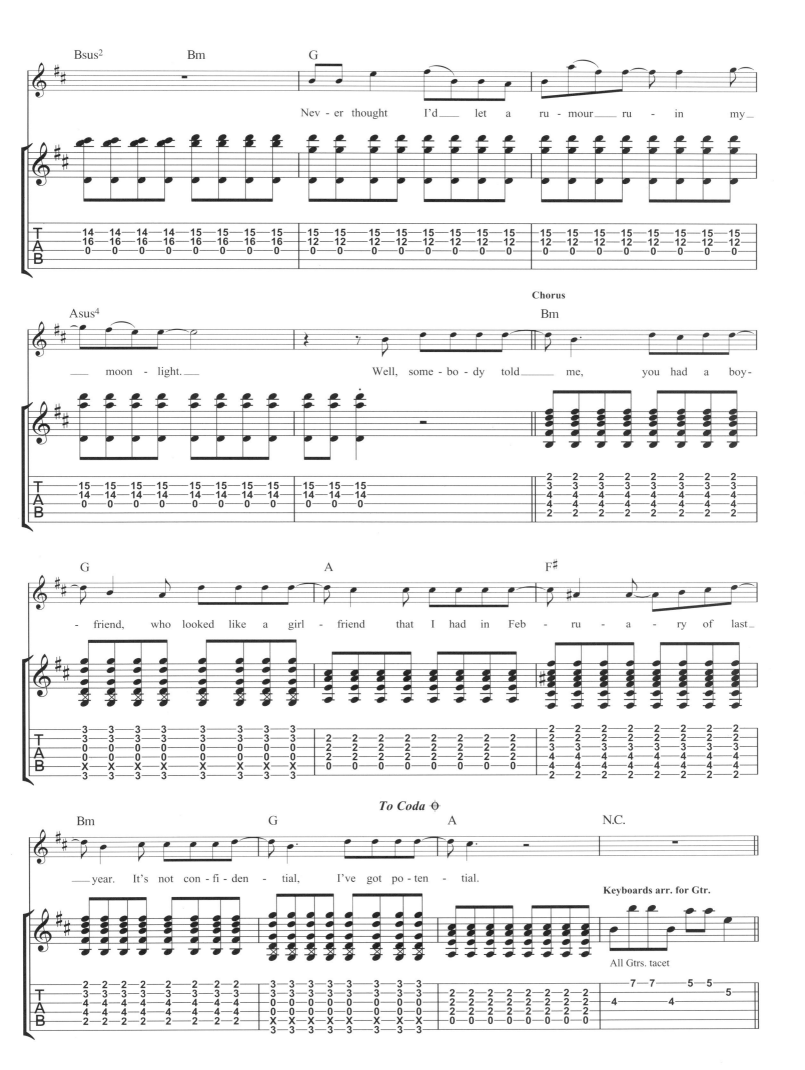

147

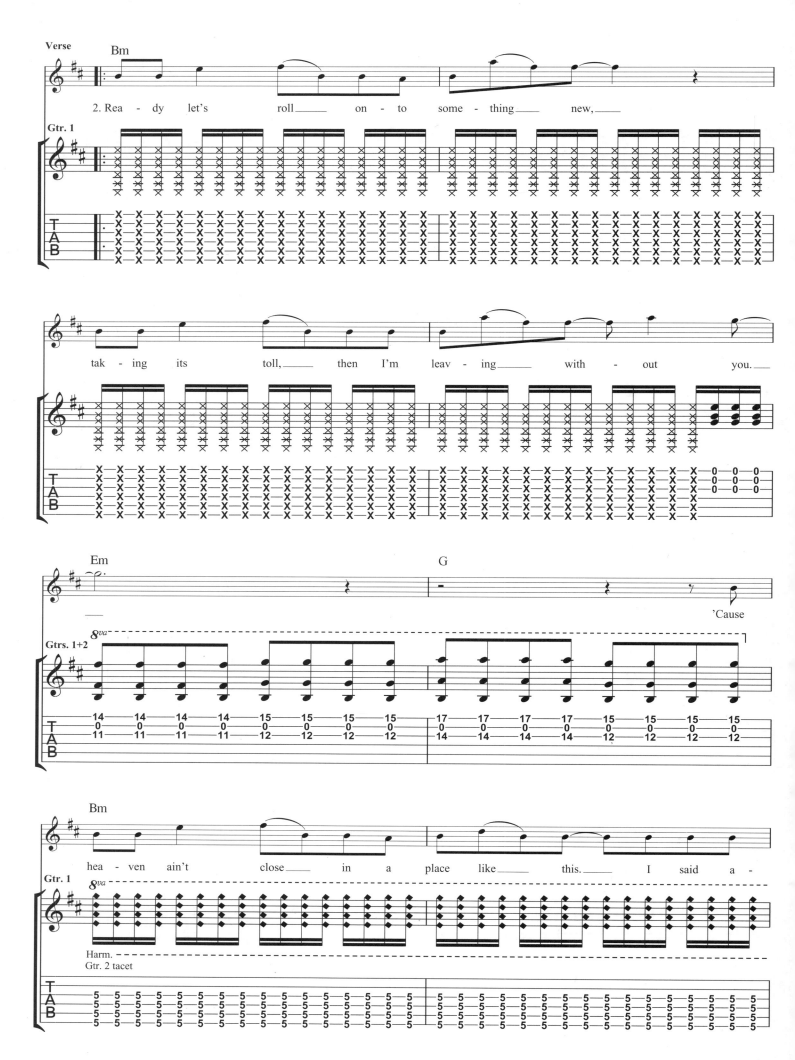

148

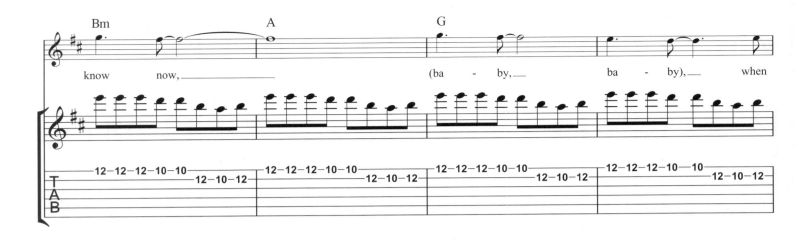

know now, _____ (ba - by, __ ba - by), __ when

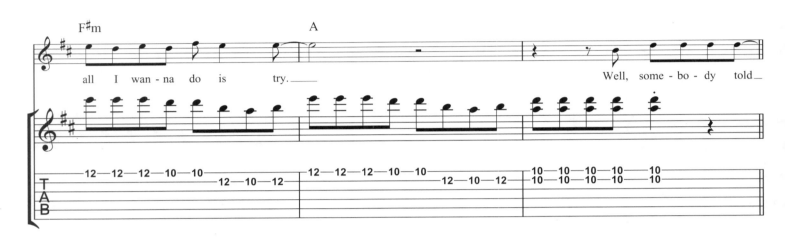

all I wan - na do is try. ___ Well, some - bo - dy told __

Chorus

___ me, you had a boy - friend, who looked like a girl - friend that I had in Feb-

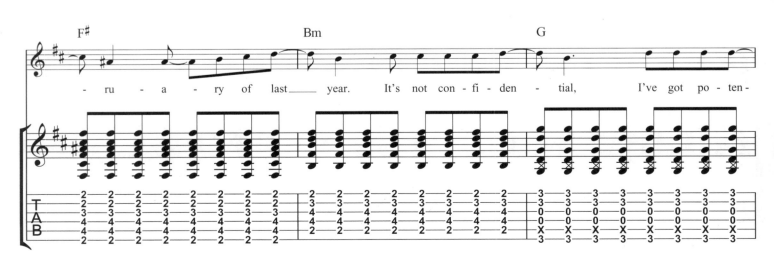

- ru - a - ry of last ___ year. It's not con - fi - den - tial, I've got po - ten-

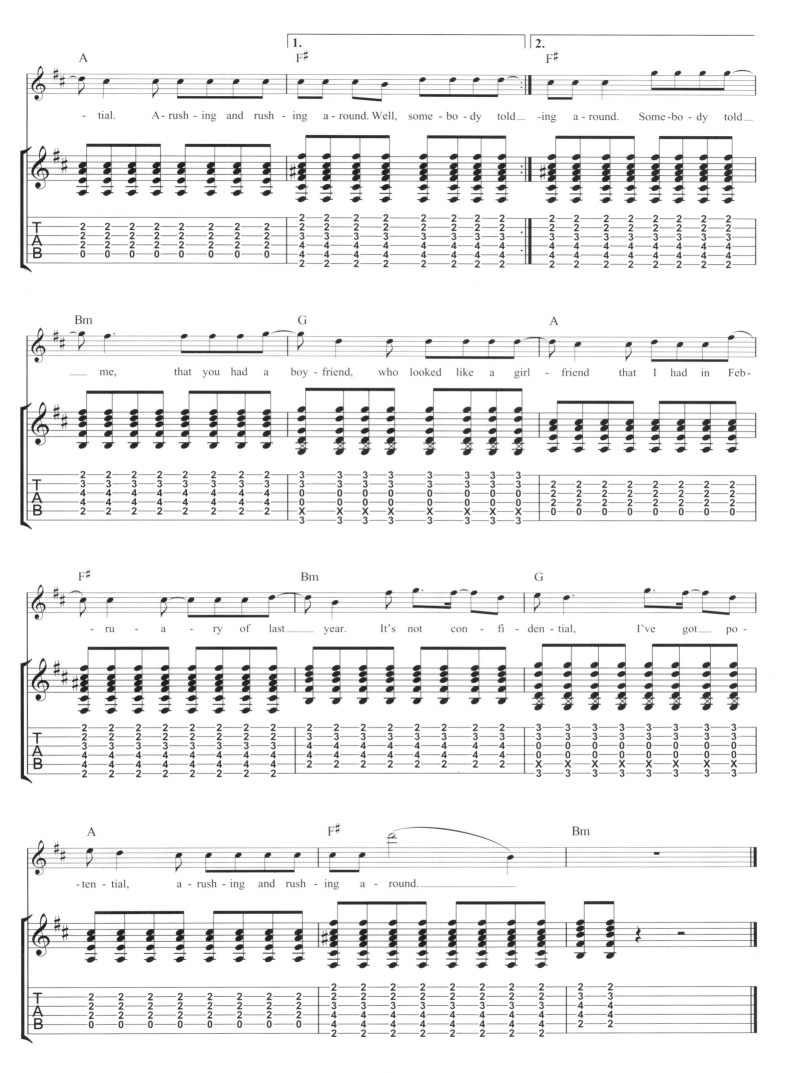

TALK TALK TALK

WORDS & MUSIC BY WILLIAM BROWN, SAMUEL PRESTON, CHARLES STANLEY & JAMES GREGORY

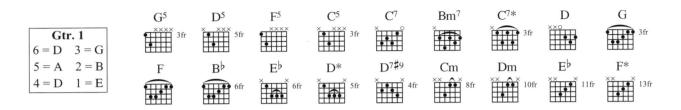

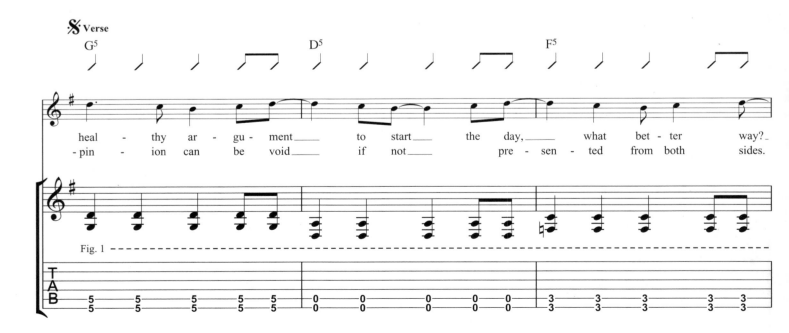

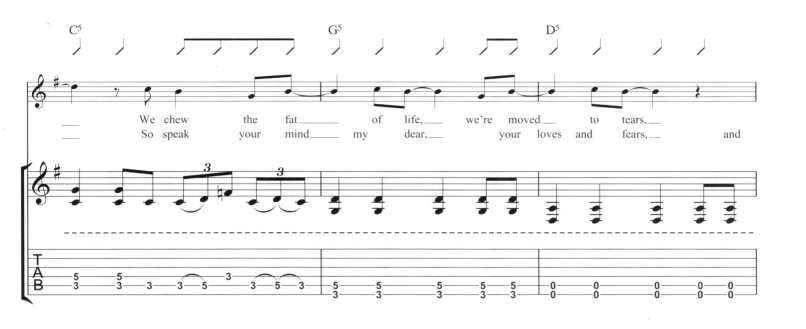

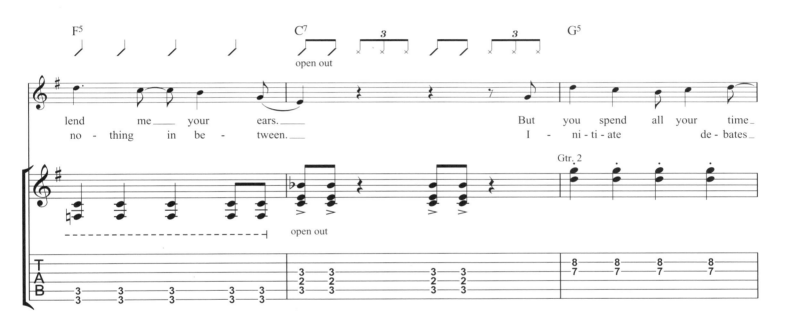

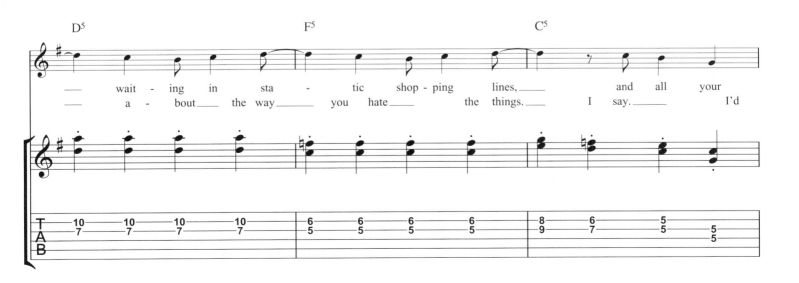

trou - ble - some _ de - bates _ are solved in gloss - y ma - ga - zines. _

ra - ther that _ than spend _ a - no - ther min - ute kill - ing time. _

Pre-chorus

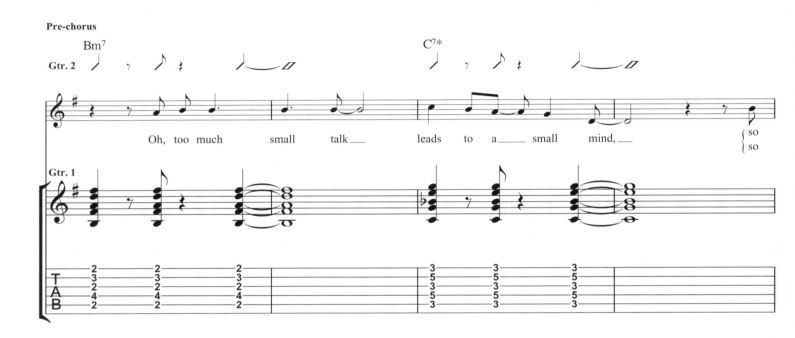

Oh, too much small talk _ leads to a _ small mind, _ so so

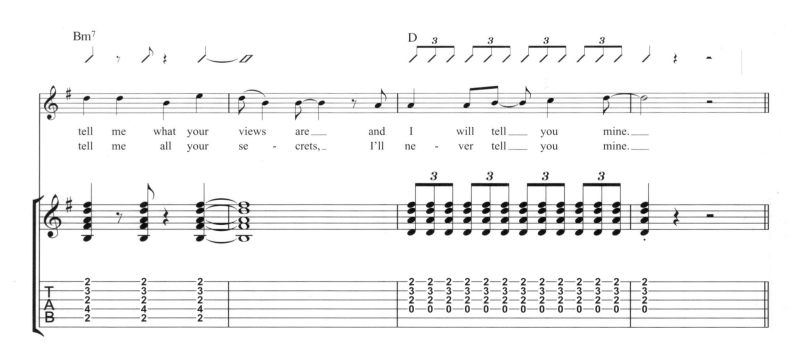

tell me what your views are _ and I will tell _ you mine. _

tell me all your se - crets, _ I'll ne - ver tell _ you mine. _

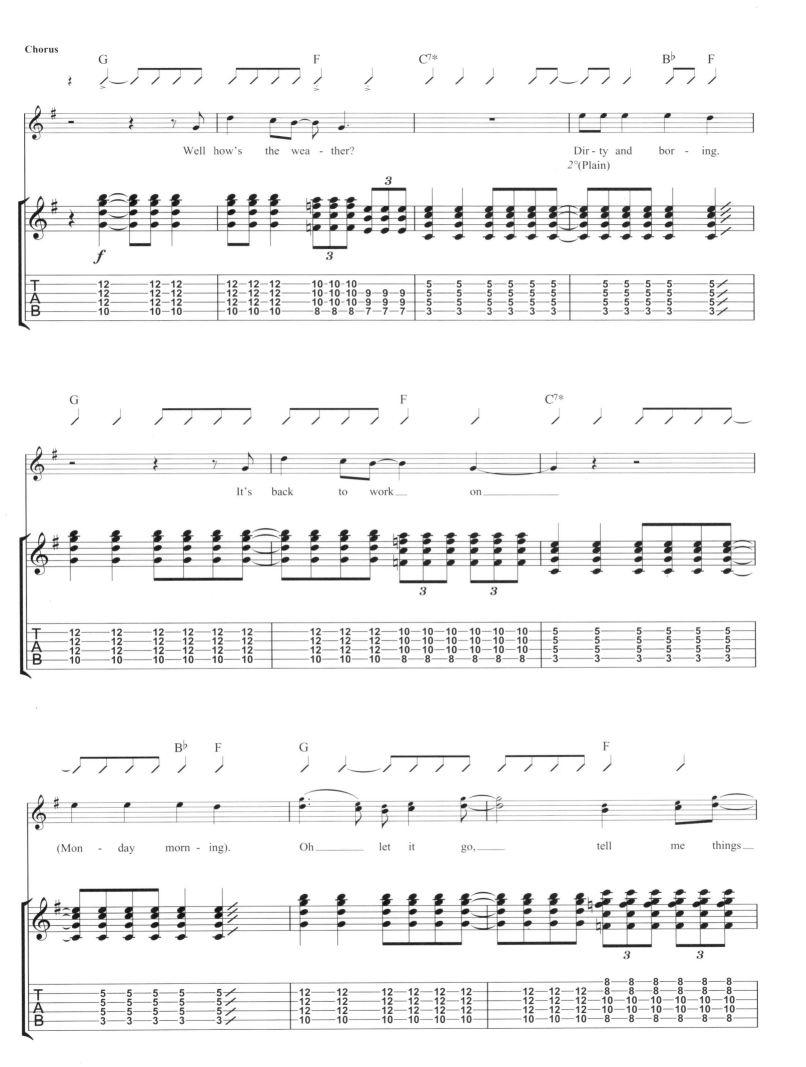

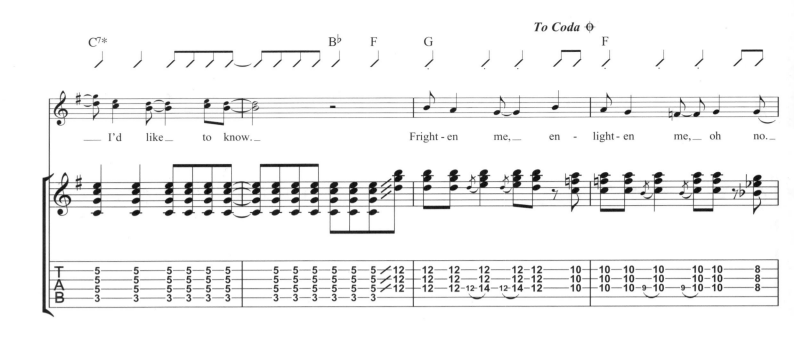

I'd like__ to know.__ Fright-en me,__ en-light-en me,__ oh no.__

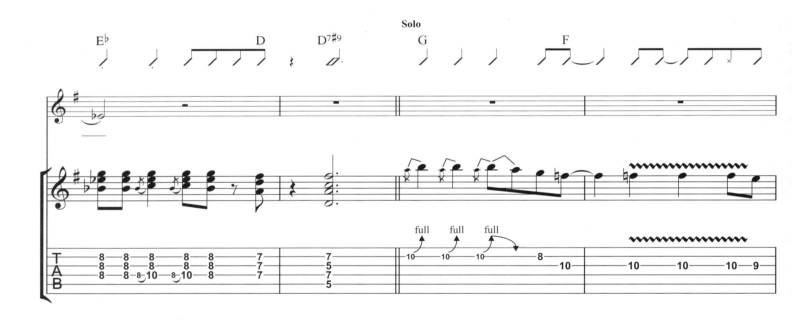

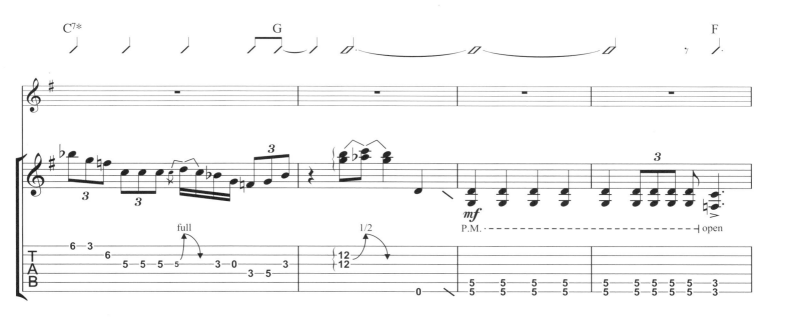

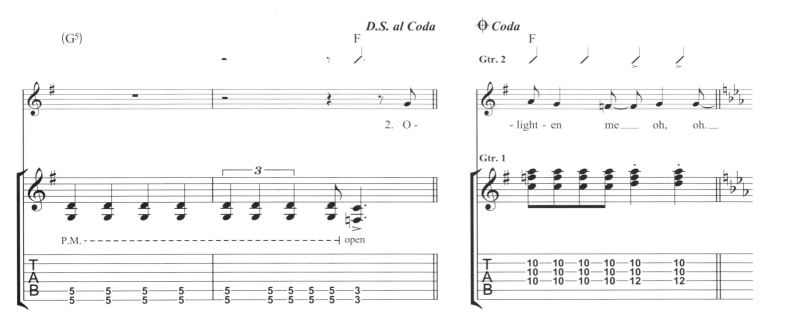

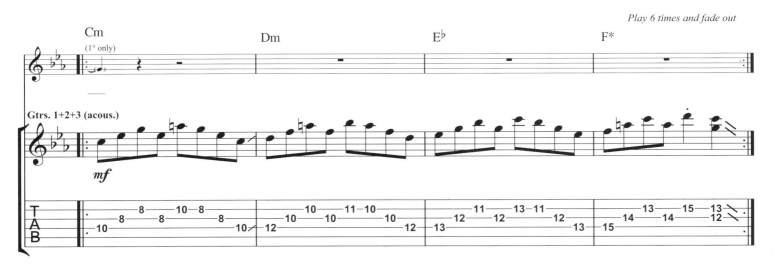

STUMBLE AND FALL

WORDS & MUSIC BY JOHNNY BORRELL & BJÖRN ÄGREN

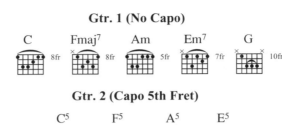

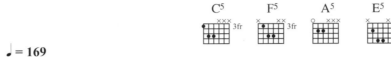

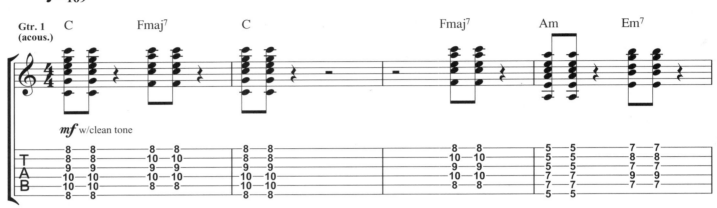

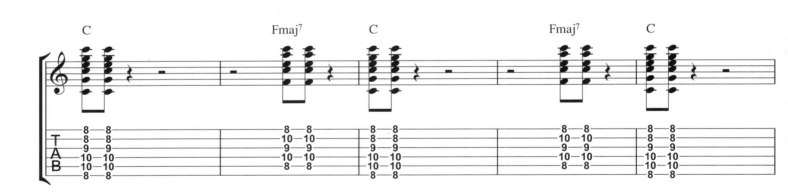

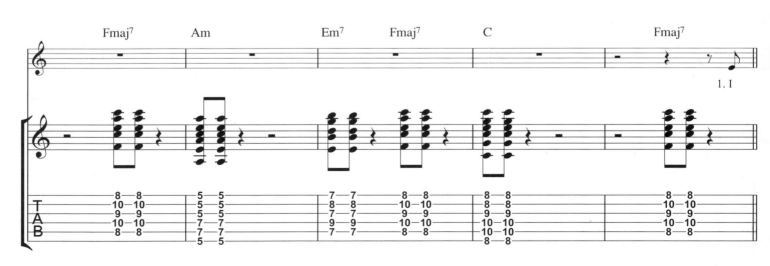

*Gtr. 1 chords

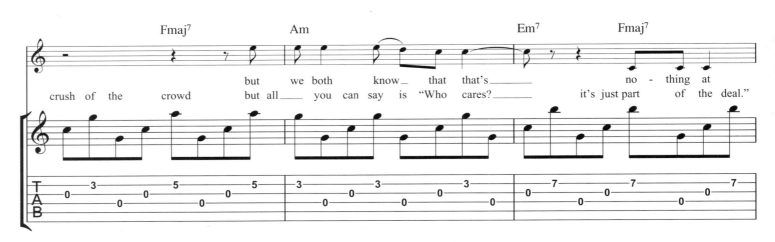

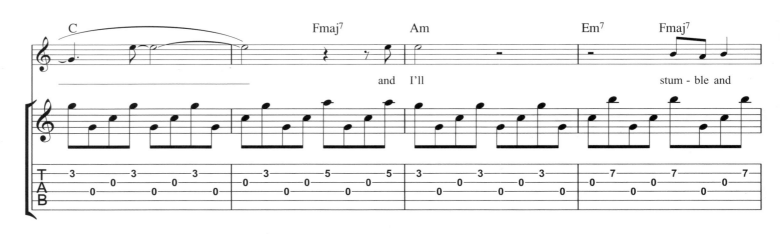

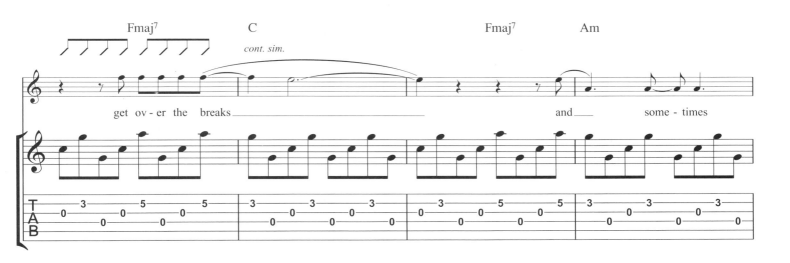

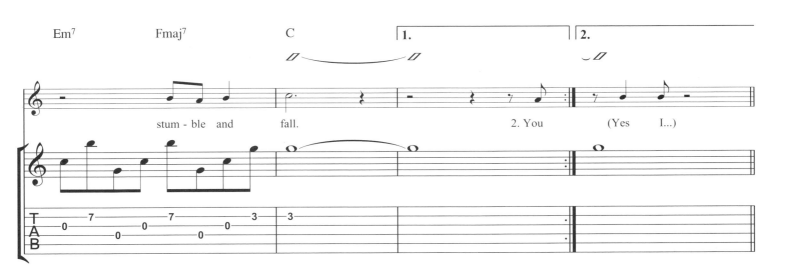

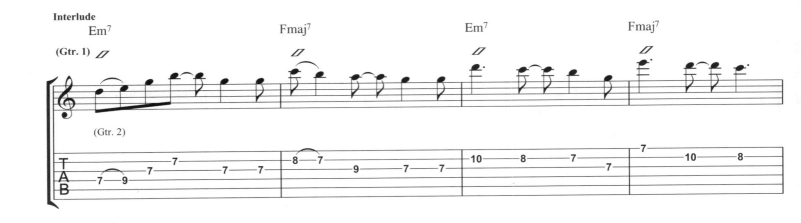

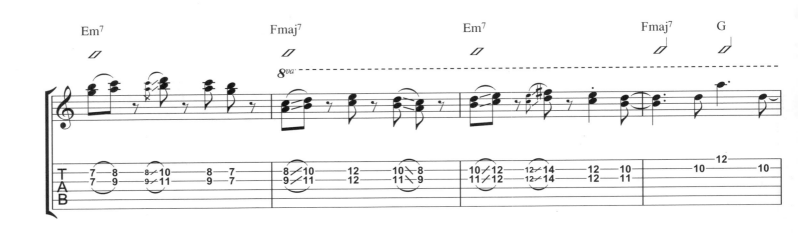

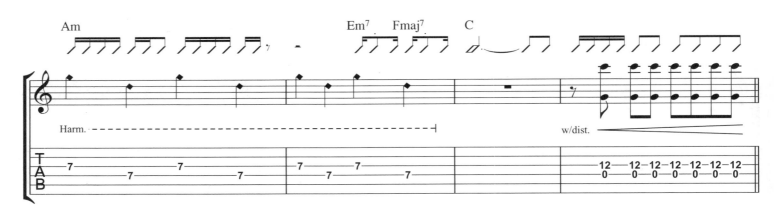

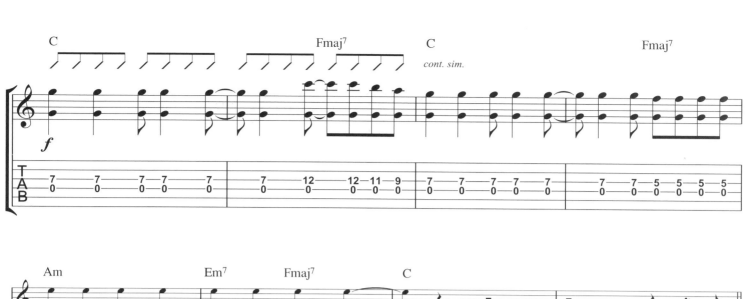

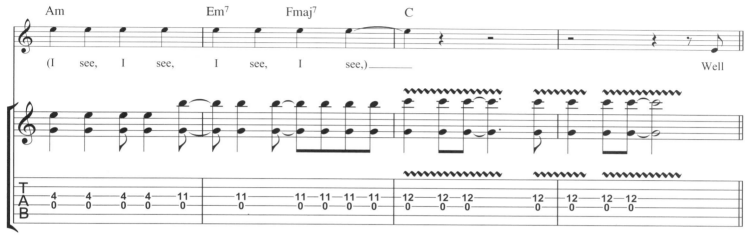

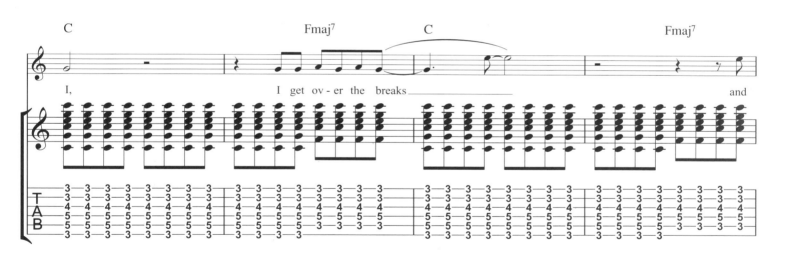

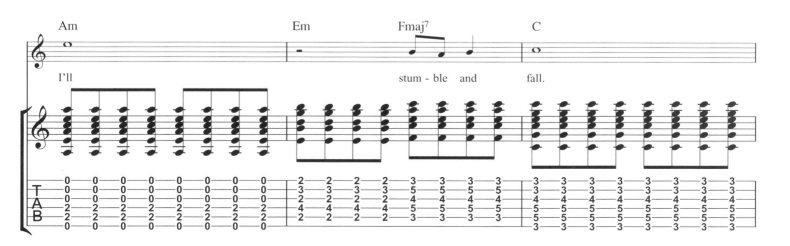

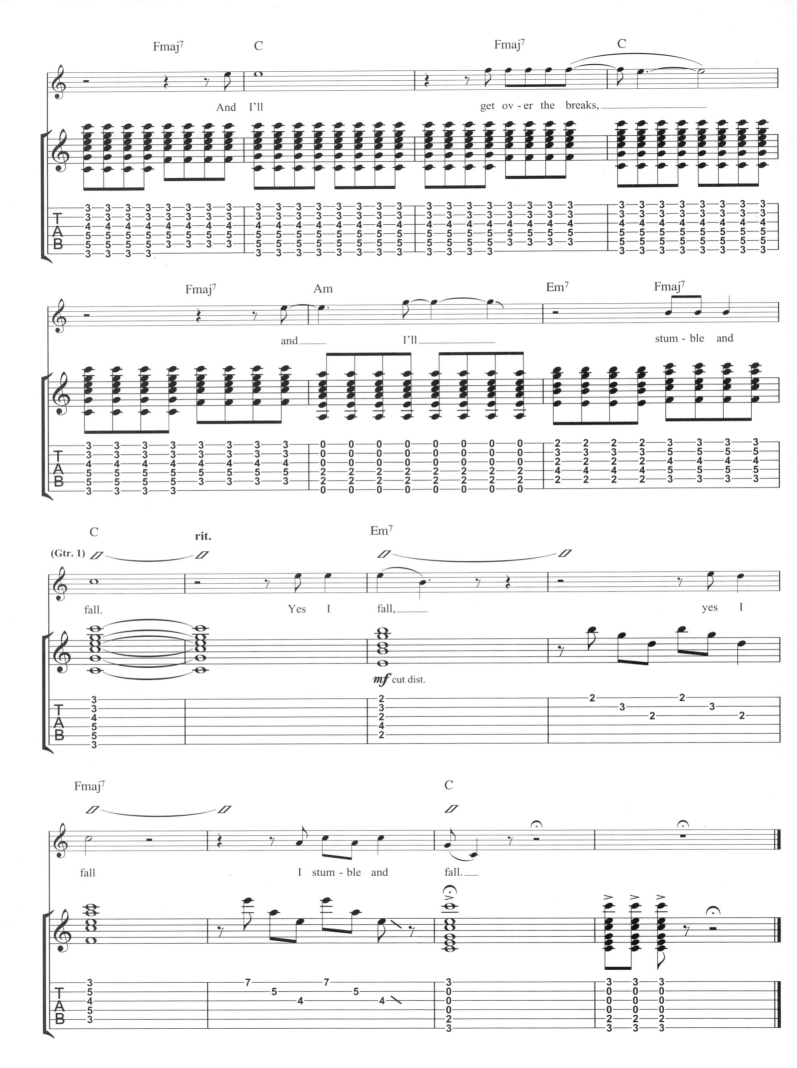

THRU THE GLASS

WORDS & MUSIC BY WILL SOUTH, TOM WELHAM, ADAM WILSON & BRENDON JAMES

all I wan-na see,___ but there's such a lot of bag - gage.___

Chorus

You got us in - to this, so get us out of this,___ get us out of this,___

___ get us out of.___ You got us in - to this, so get us out of this,___

___ get us out of this,___ oh get us out.___

167

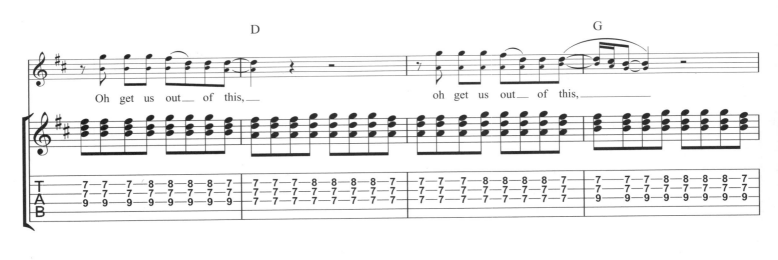

D

G

Oh get us out __ of this, __

oh get us out __ of this, __

To Coda ⊕

Bm

F#

Gtr. 3

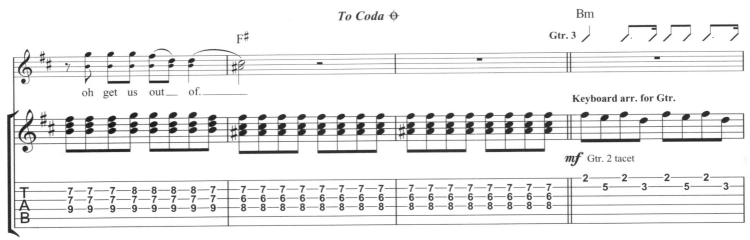

oh get us out __ of.

Keyboard arr. for Gtr.

mf Gtr. 2 tacet

G

D

F#

Gon - na lose __ con -

Bm

G

-trol, look down, scream out __ loud, let the oth - ers sort __

VERTIGO
WORDS & MUSIC BY U2

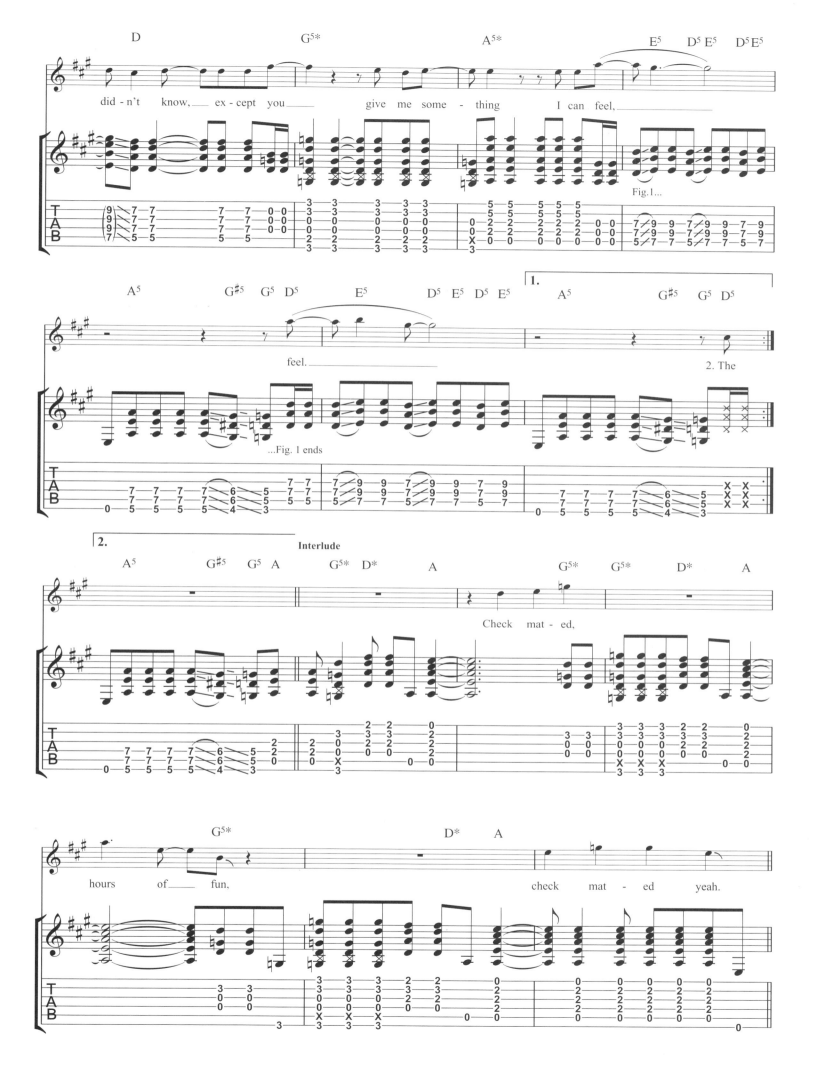